In memory of

John Gray, Emergency Physician

1965 – 2019

Paul Hanley, Radiologist

1957 – 2020

# TOGETHER

## 2020–2022

TUCK GOH

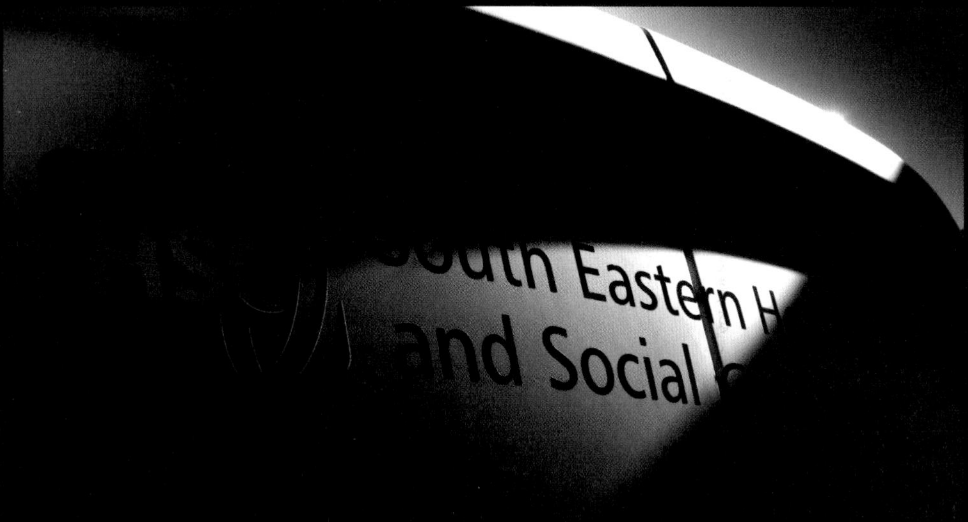

Eastern
and Social

This book reflects some of the stories and experiences of staff across the South Eastern Health and Social Care Trust in Northern Ireland during the COVID-19 pandemic. It is a heartfelt and fitting tribute to all those who gave so much in caring for our patients, clients and families. Everyone played their part and came together – we had each other's back during such challenging and difficult times – we will never forget.

Thank you for all that you do every day.

Roisin Coulter

Chief Executive
South Eastern Health and Social Care Trust
Northern Ireland

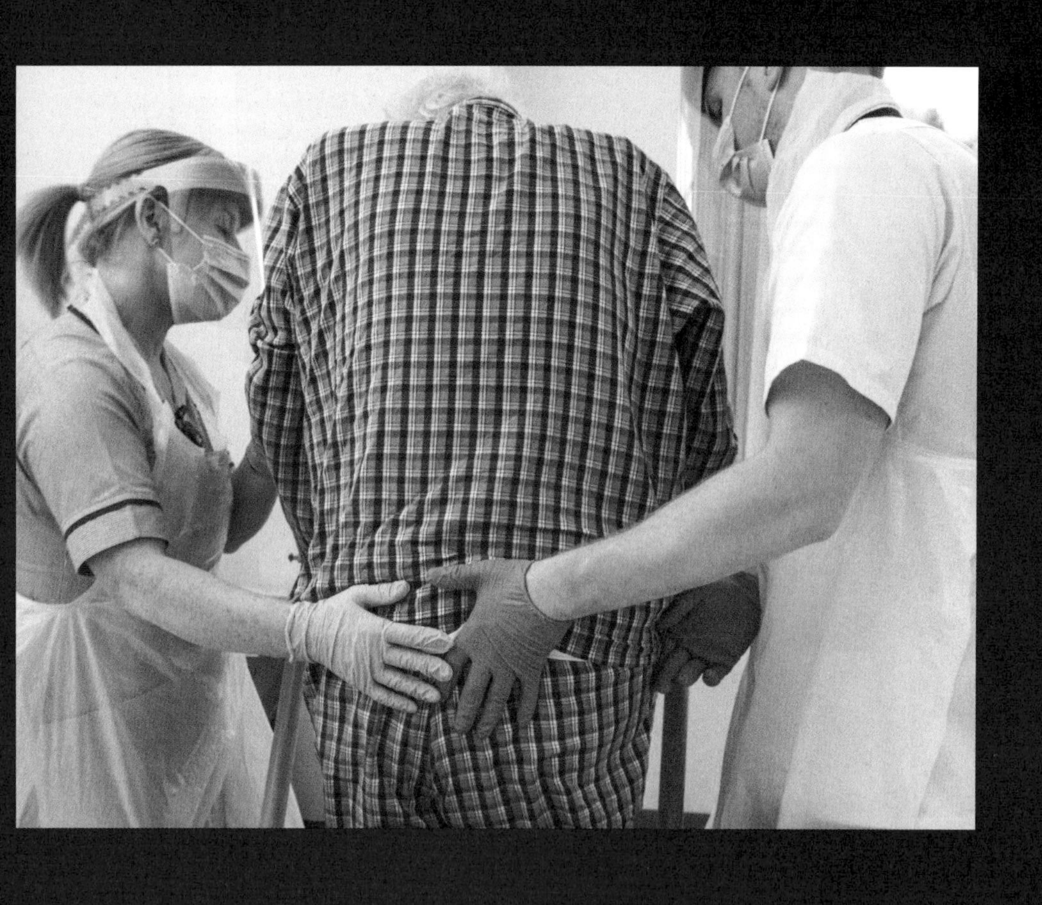

One of the first photographs to be taken was of the empty waiting room of the Emergency Department where I work. This was of course highly unusual for a department that had an attendance of 108,000 patients the year before. It was mid-March 2020, the beginning of the COVID-19 pandemic in Northern Ireland. It was an anxious moment for those of us working at the front line. Was this the calm before the storm? Would our corridors soon be overwhelmed by very ill patients?

These patients did arrive but fortunately not en masse. But working life changed for all of us.

PPE was the in-word. We changed daily into scrubs in newly installed Portakabins. Mobile phones were put into sealed plastic bags. We came home to go straight into showers. The public clapped on Thursdays. We drove by walls and boards displaying messages of support and gratitude for the NHS. Some of us even chose to live separately to isolate ourselves to protect our loved ones.

The images in this photobook are reflective snapshots of the experience for staff and patients in the South Eastern Health and Social Care Trust during the pandemic. Some highlight compassion and care, some show happiness and joy, a few display anxiety and isolation, but most show staff going about their daily tasks with focus and dedication in the way they know best.

For all of us, the pandemic has transformed the way we work and the way we delivered essential services. We had to demonstrate flexibility and adaptability in the light of new challenges. There will be many memories and stories to relate of individual and collective experiences during this unusual period for the National Health Service. The images in this book are some of them.

Tuck Goh

Associate Specialist
Emergency Department
Ulster Hospital
Dundonald

SPLASH SHIELD.

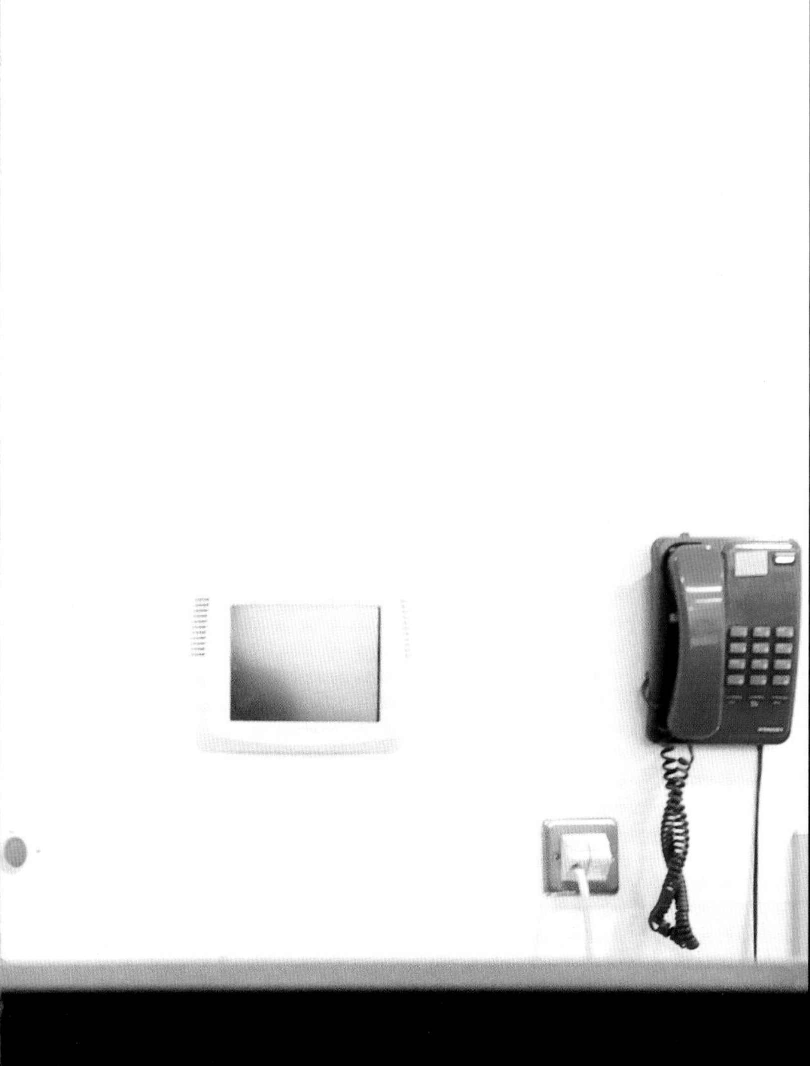

Children's Play Area
CAUTION
WET
FLOOR
CAUTION
WET
FLOOR

## EMERGENCY DEPARTMENT

February 2020 saw fear and anxiety at an all-time high in the Emergency Department. Fear for what was ahead, for family members, for colleagues and whether we had the skill set needed to care for patients adequately with COVID-19. Emotions were further heightened by what we were seeing and hearing in the media about other Emergency Departments being overwhelmed.

Initially, our department was quickly reconfigured into Red and Green zones. Very soon we realised that this Red zone was too small for both the numbers attending and that our sickest patients were likely to be those with potential COVID-19. So, over a 24-hour period the department was flipped with the Red zone being moved to include a sizable section of the department to allow for adequate capacity and to include a paediatric COVID-19 area. All patients were screened at the front door on arrival and signposted to the correct designated area.

To reduce the risk to our vulnerable patients, doors were added to cubicles within the Red zone. Our Minor Injuries service and clinics were relocated to Outpatients to allow for more space.

As lockdown in the summer 2020 ended there was now a need to increase capacity for non COVID-19 patients attending. The department underwent a further reconfiguration to accommodate this.

Over the following year there have been peaks and troughs of COVID-19 attendances with new variants emerging alongside the yearly winter pressures resulting in an increasing challenging environment.

Jenny Nicholson
Lead Nurse

Welcome to the
Oasis Restaurant
SIR
CAUTION
WET
FLOOR
SIR
CAUTION
WET
FLOOR

Waiting Area D

www.eb-med.com
Direct Splash

## PPE Update – 3rd April 2020

In line with increasing public prevalence of COVID-19, the Public Health Agencies and Royal Colleges updated PPE guidance on 2nd April 2020.

From 3rd April, PPE rules in the Ulster Hospital Emergency Department will be as follows:

**GREEN ZONE**

Fluid-shield surgical mask

Goggles : When leaving the green zone, these should be placed in the dirty bucket for disinfection and re-use

Plastic apron and disposable gloves: Single use for each direct patient contact

**RED ZONE**

Fluid-shield surgical mask

Visor: Disposed of when leaving the red zone

Plastic apron and disposable gloves: Single use for each direct patient contact

**PERFORMING OR ASSISTING WITH AEROSOL GENERATING PROCEDURES (AGPs)**

FFP3 Mask

Visor

Disposable long-sleeved gown and disposable gloves

Dispose of and replace PPE after patient contact

**SPECIAL NOTE**

Once it becomes necessary to perform AGPs outside rooms with closed doors (consultant decision), AGP PPE will be worn in the whole majors/resus area. This decision will be made clear by the Consultant and Nurse in Charge.

free

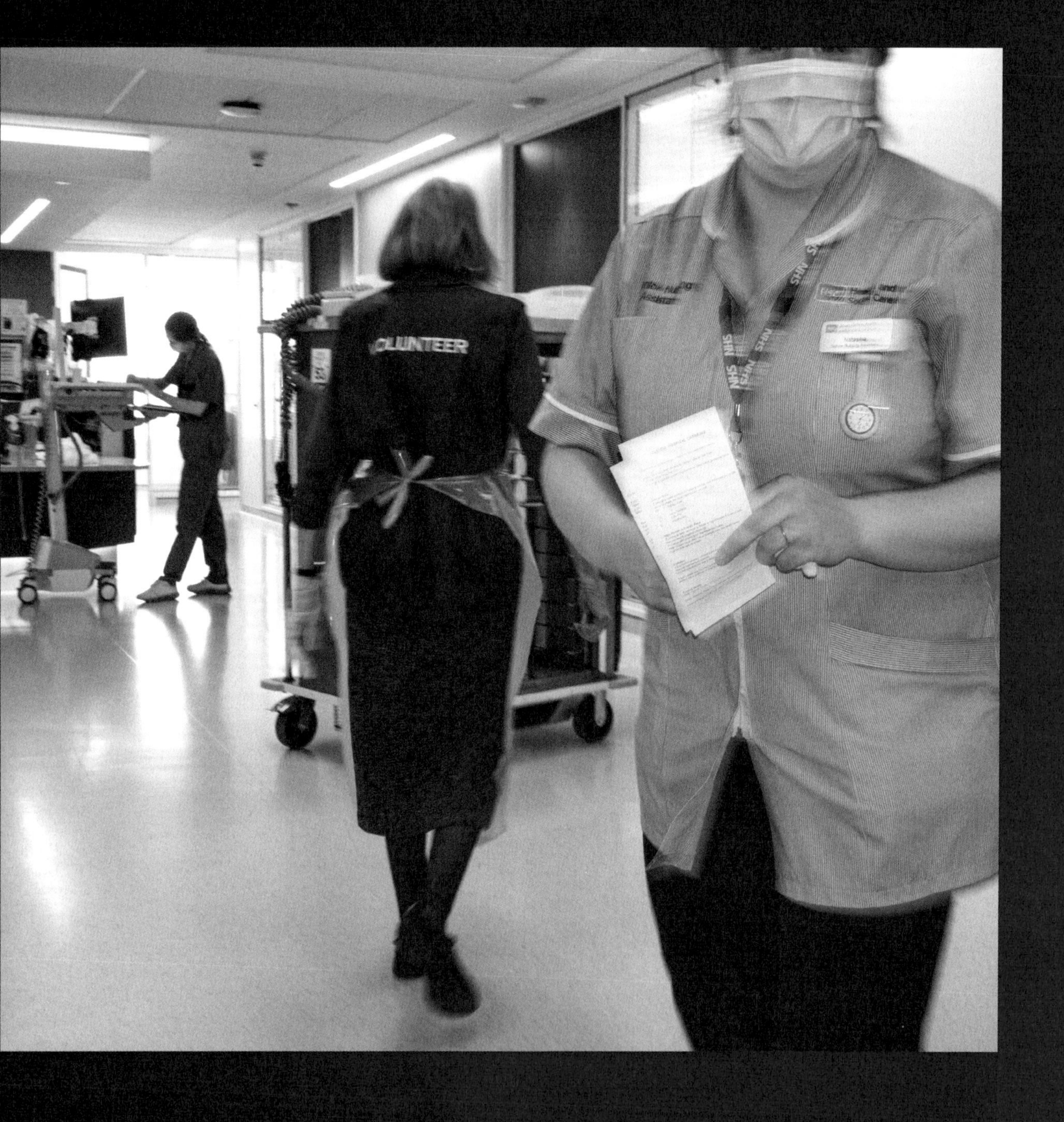
VOLUNTEER
NHS

CHARLES
DANGER
Radiation
risk
Dräger
ROTHBAND
124/76 (86)

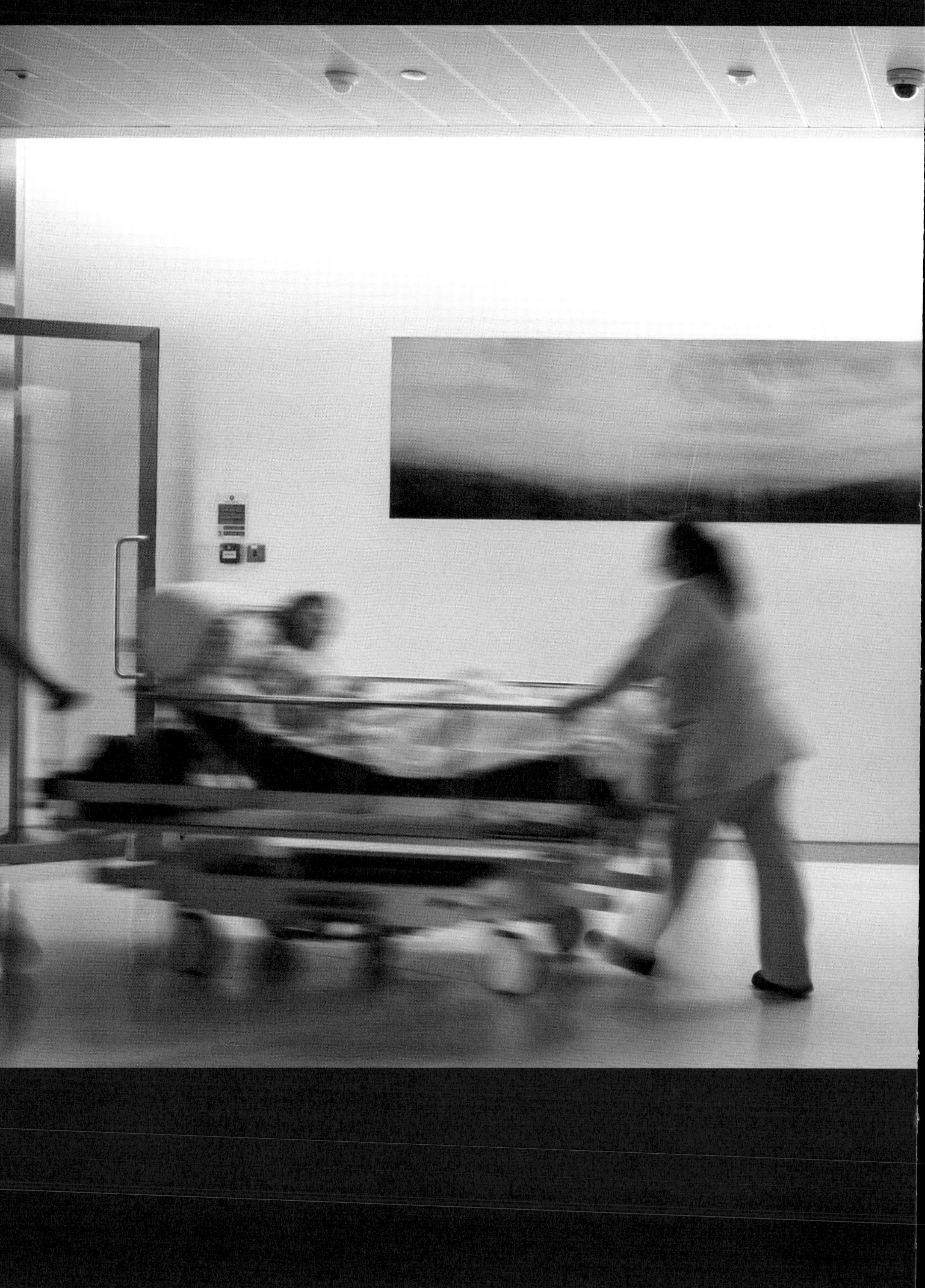

Emerg
Depart
Main Ent
Parking
Pay Mach
Eastern Health
ocial Care Trust
All Emerge
artment F
o Report

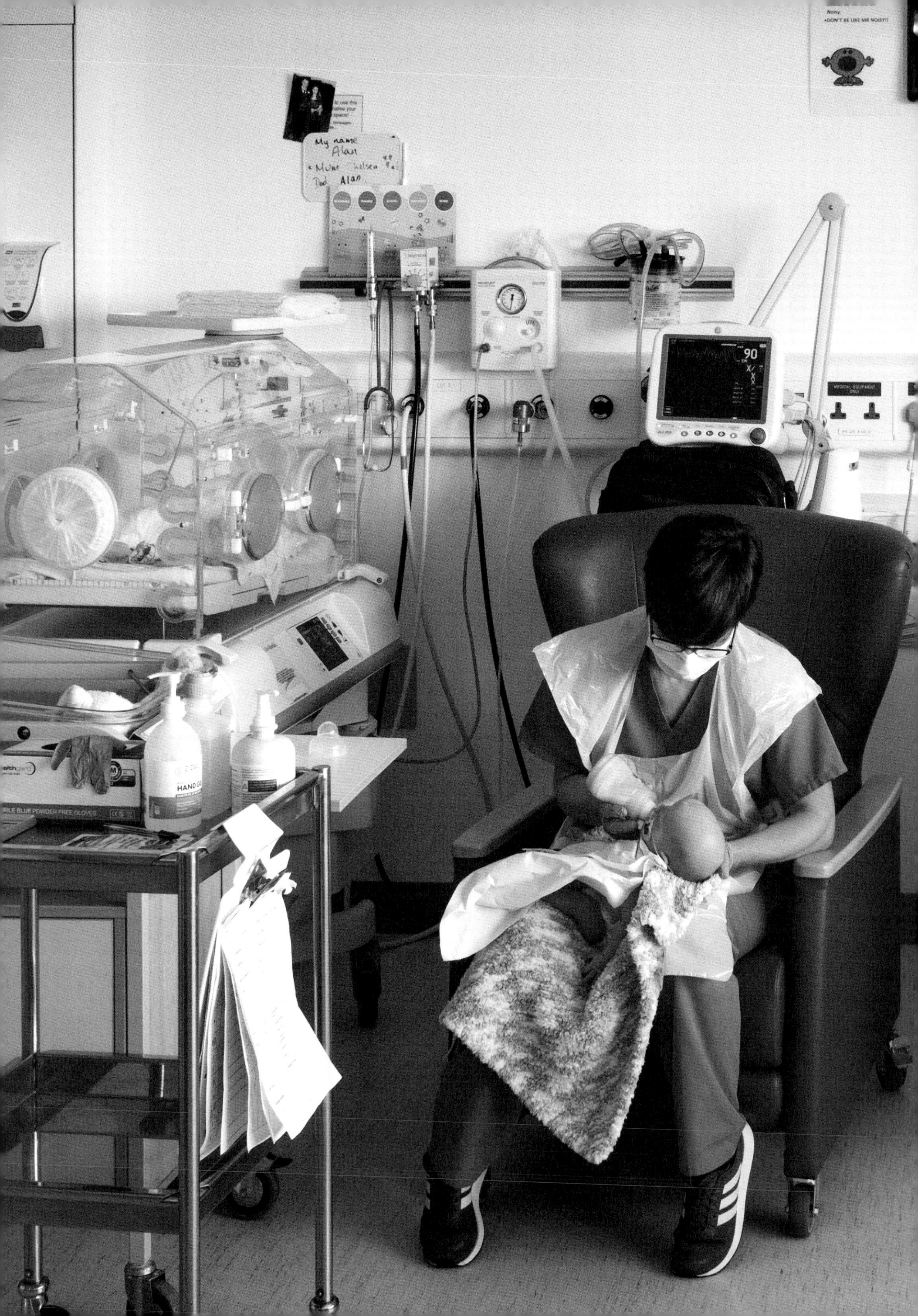

Noisy.
•DON'T BE LIKE MR NOISY!!
My name Alan
• Mum helsea
Dad Alan
90
MEDICAL EQUIPMENT ONLY
HAND GE
RILE BLUE POWDER FREE GLOVES

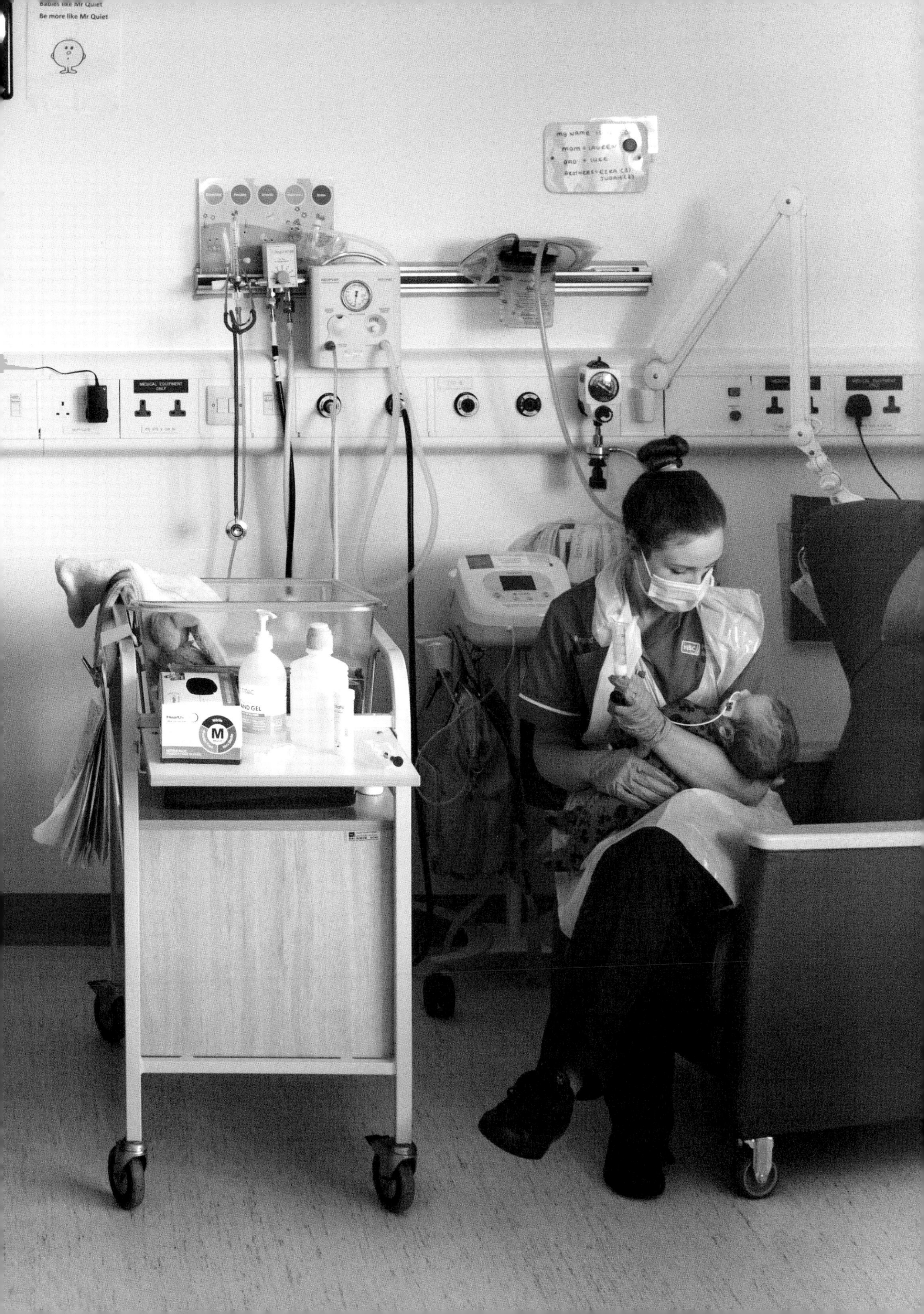
Babies like Mr Quiet
Be more like Mr Quiet
MEDICAL EQUIPMENT ONLY
HAND GEL
M

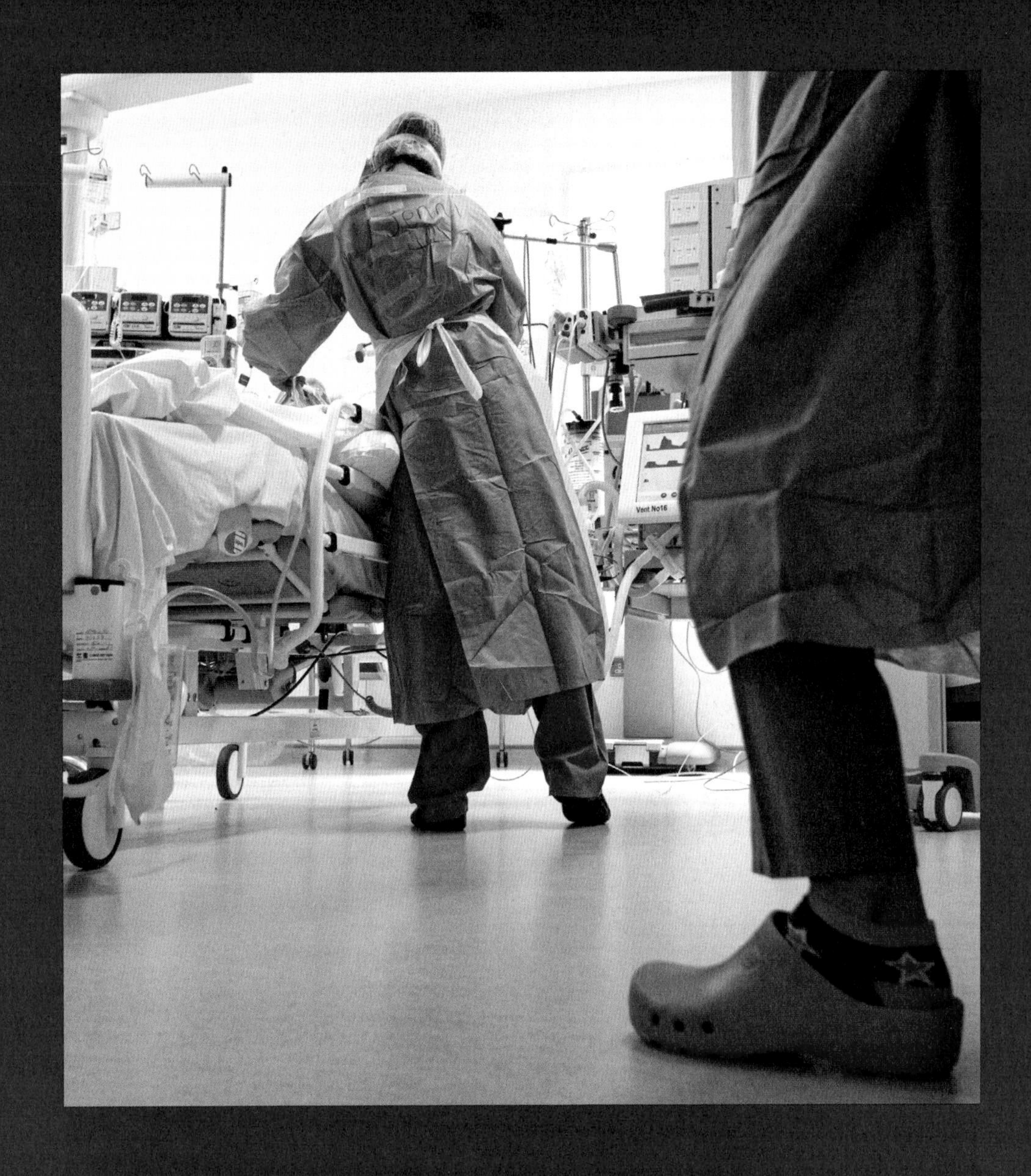
Vent No16

## INTENSIVE CARE UNIT

In the reconfiguration for the pandemic, our ICU had to double its capacity by overflowing into the nearby recovery ward, enabling us to care for both COVID-19 and non COVID-19 critically ill patients. Many of the COVID-19 patients admitted to ICU required maximal support as many of them had multi-organ failure.

Workload became heavy as patients needed turned into the prone position to assist oxygenation and many needed dialysis due to renal failure. Fortunately, staff from other areas within the Trust were redeployed to assist us during this period. We would not have coped without their support.

Wearing full PPE for up to 12 hours at a time was physically and mentally exhausting. It also had an impact on how we were able to communicate effectively with our patients, their relatives and each other. We found ways to improve communication with family members, such as virtual visiting, daily phone updates and round the clock availability to answer their concerns.

We also had to develop and adapt new strategies and skills. Our psychological and emotional reserves were stretched to the limit and the management team provided us with a clinical psychologist for support.

Sadly, some patients were unable to overcome this disease and we found it difficult when family members were unable to be with their loved ones during this period. However, the joy we felt when a patient recovered will never be forgotten, and their personal stories are now permanently weaved into our memories.

Going forward, COVID-19 has made us a stronger team. Our shared experiences and our realised reliance on each other have brought us closer together.

Shauna Lynam

Lead Nurse

Pamela Gordon

Clinical Lead Sister

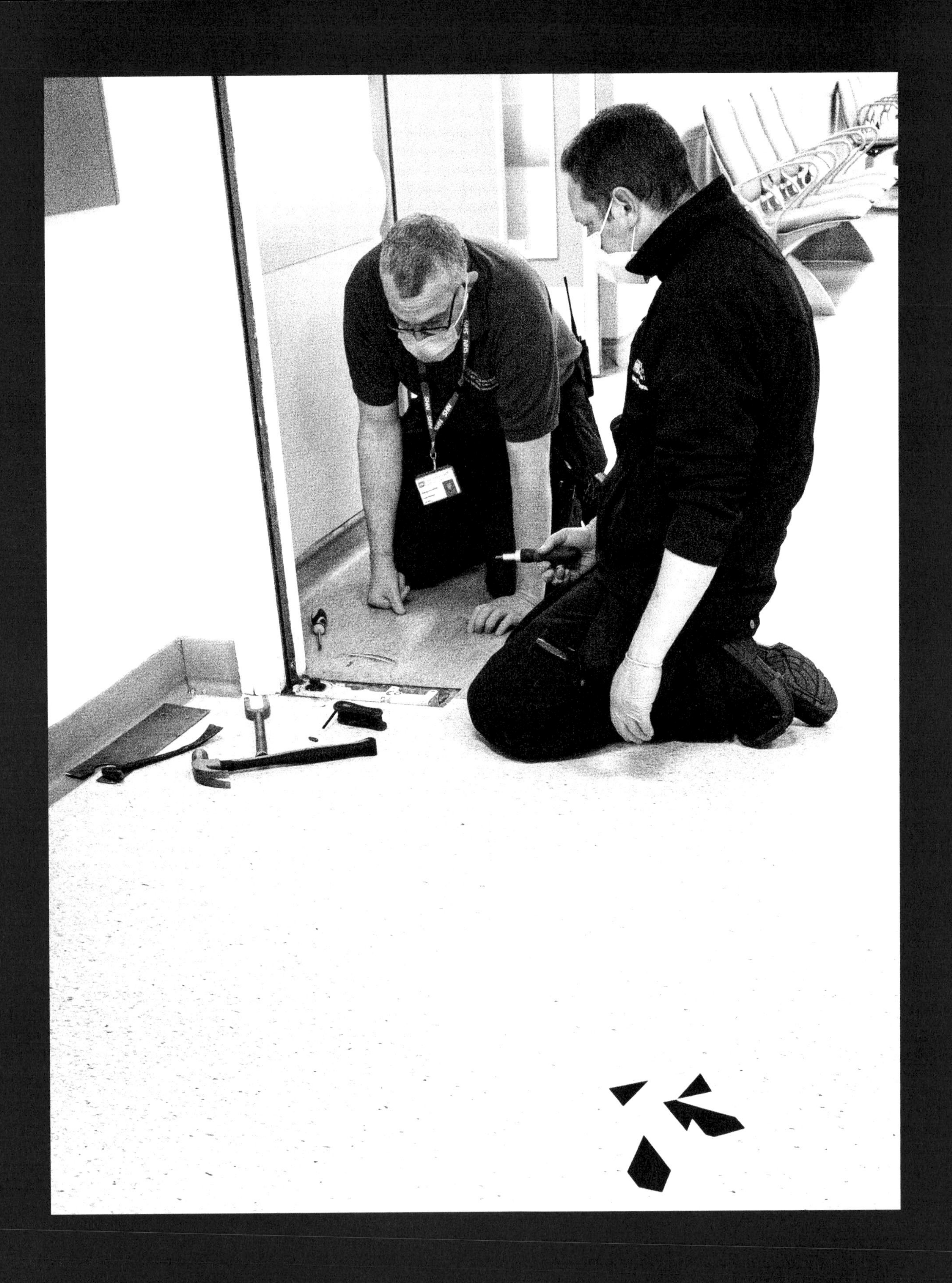

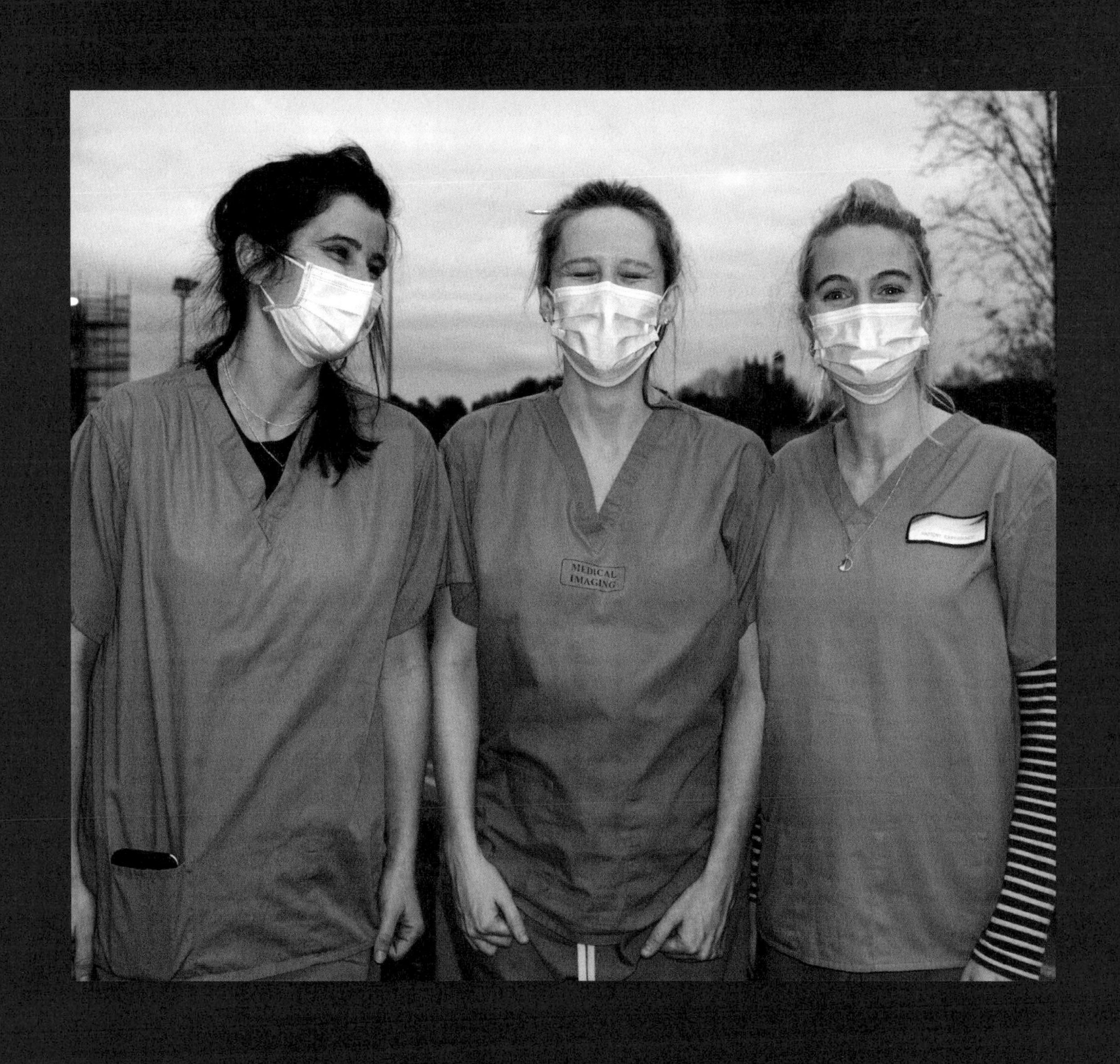
MEDICAL
IMAGING

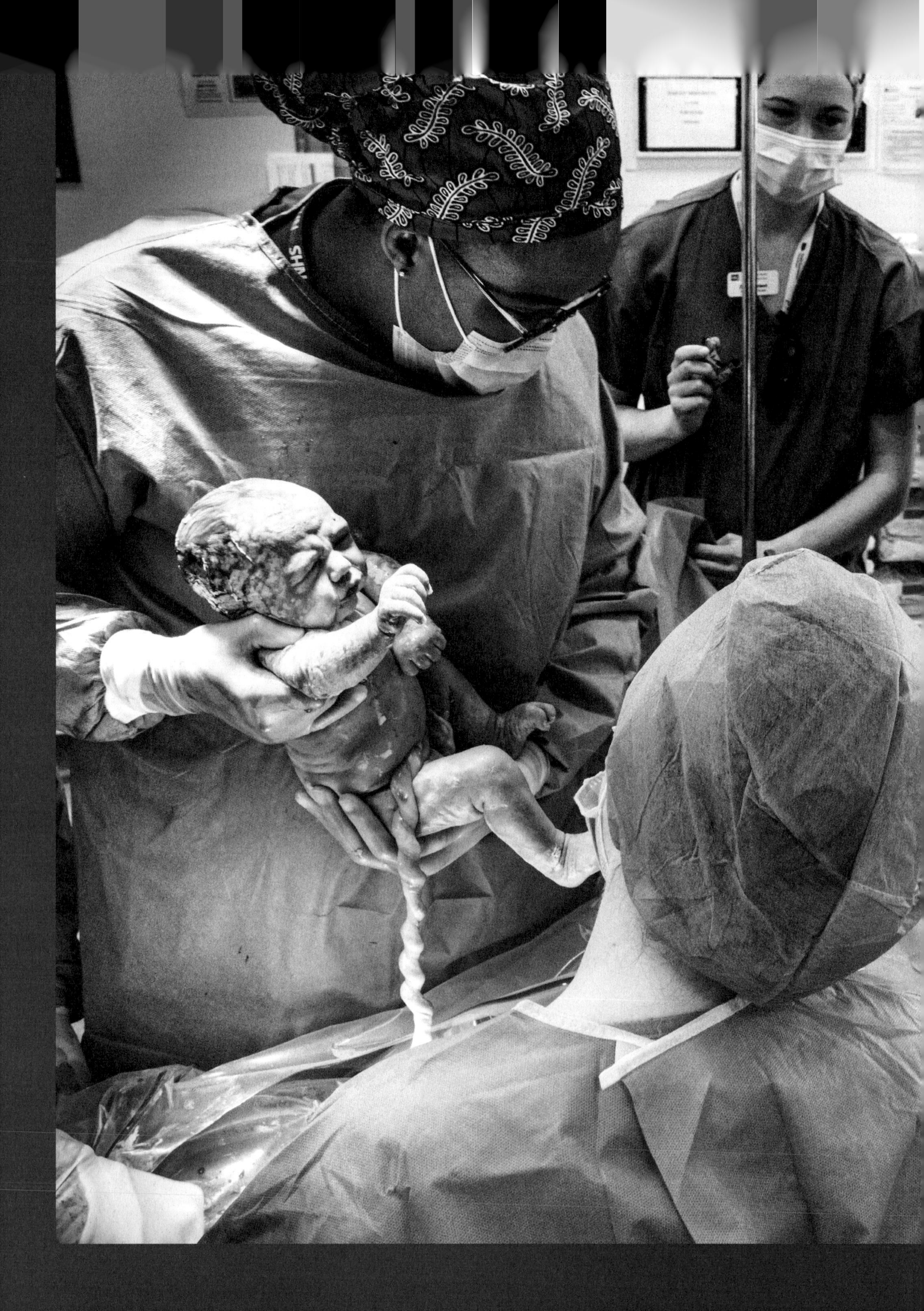

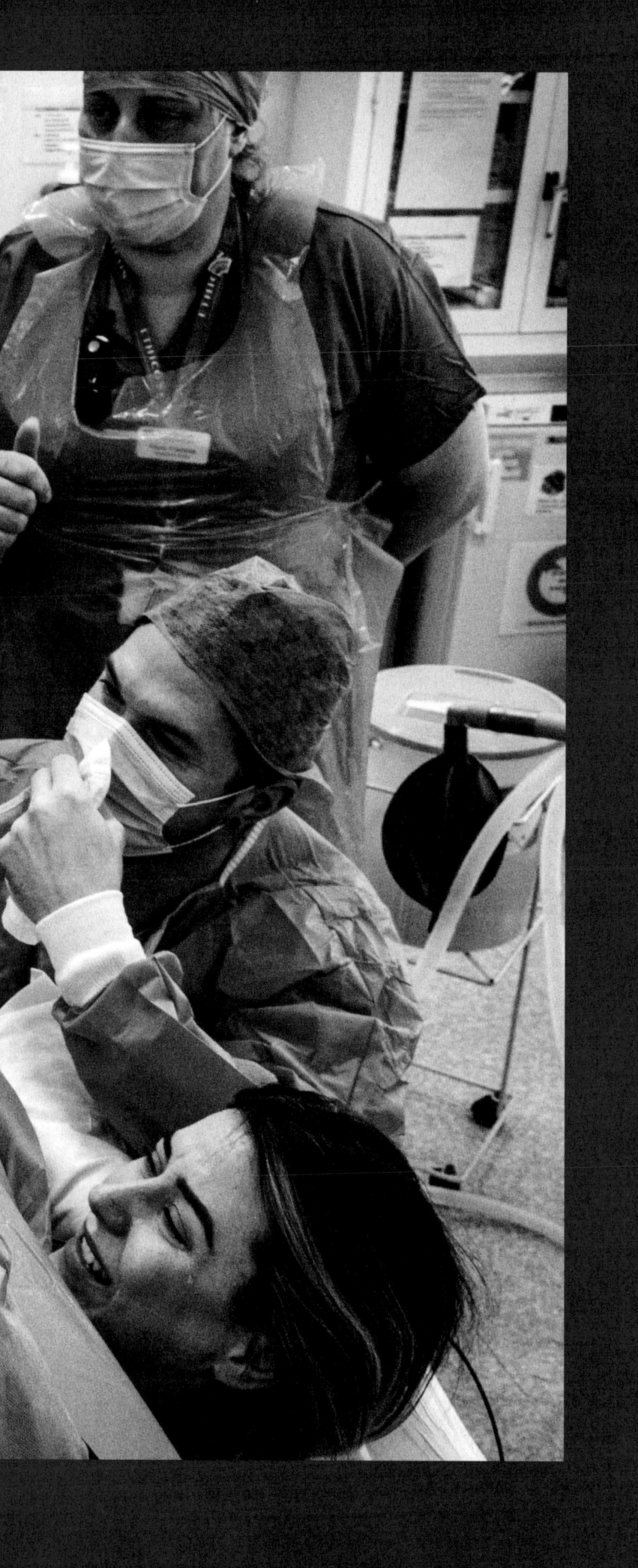

inhale
exhale

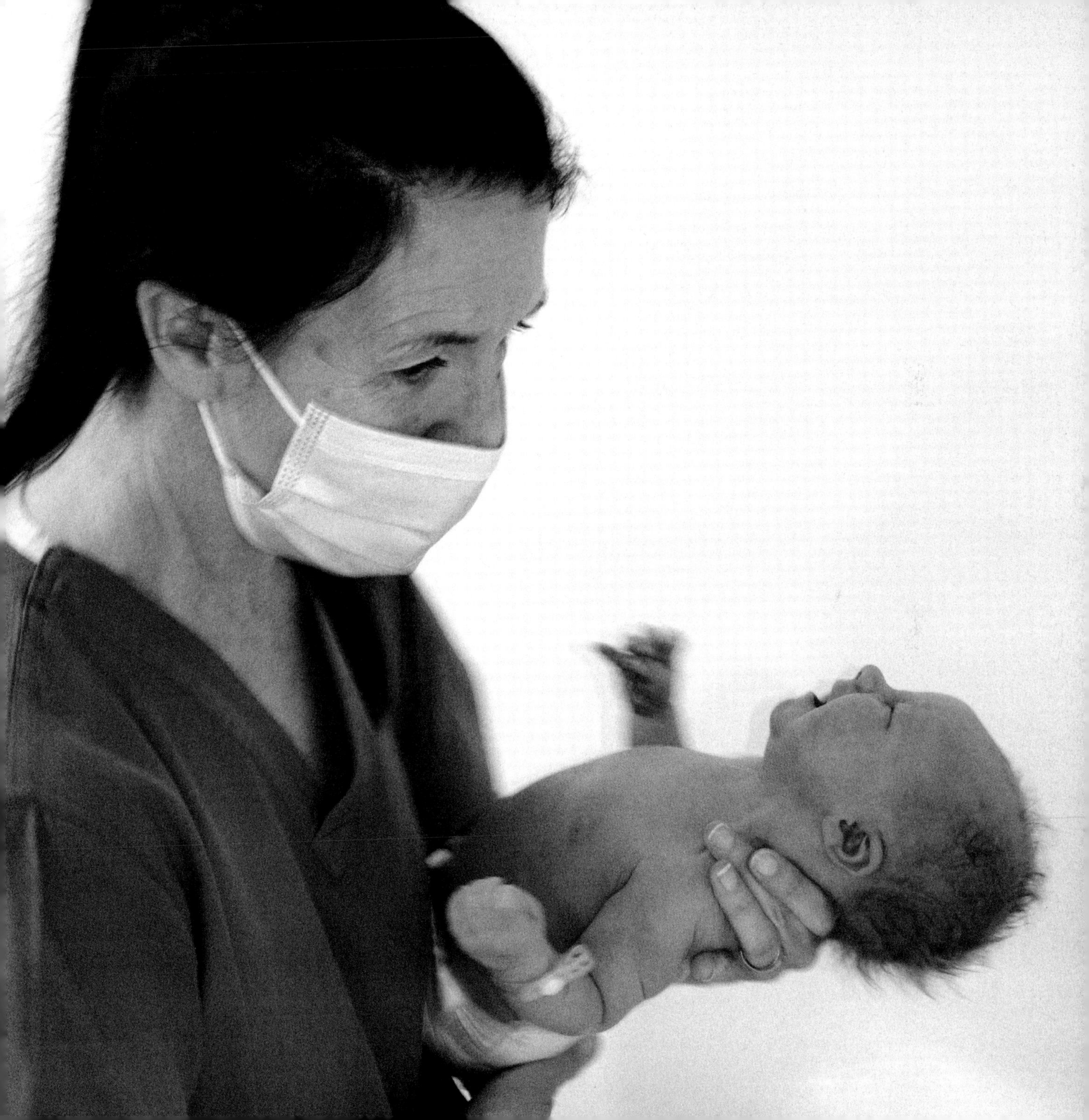

P2
8
P2
9
P2
10

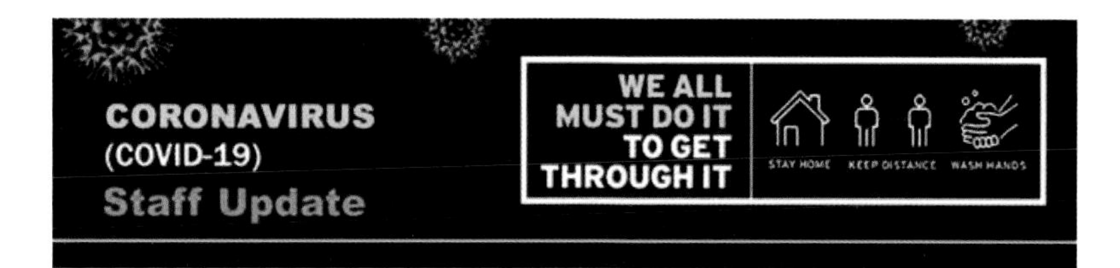


**15 April 2020**

## Staff Testing at Ards MOT Centre

We are continuing to screen and swab staff for Covid-19 at Newtownards MOT Centre, Jubilee Road.

If you, or a family member at home, are displaying symptoms of Covid-19 (high temperature/new persistent cough) then please telephone (028) 9268 0803 pressing option 1 for screening and swabbing, or option 2 for advice from a registered nurse.

Telephone lines are open 8am to 5pm

## Uniforms, scrubs & changing/showering

Arrangements are now in place for staff to access changing and showering facilities across Trust sites. Uniforms should be transported home in the bag provided and laundered according to the instructions displayed in the changing facilities.

Worn scrubs must be placed into a dissolvable bag, tied securely and placed into the red laundry bag available in all changing areas. No uniforms or Scrubs should be worn out in a public setting. Further information on showering and changing facilities can be viewed by clicking here

## Catering

Staff restaurants have re-opened after Easter with free food and beverages, and everyone is reminded of the need to practice social distancing whilst eating food in the staff canteens. The chairs and tables have been spaced out to facilitate this. It is recommended where possible that staff take their food from the canteen to their staff room or other appropriate place.

## Switch off Your Bluetooth in Clinical areas

Staff who have the Stop COVID19 App on their phone are reminded that they should turn their Bluetooth off temporarily while wearing PPE in clinical areas. If you do not do so, and are in contact with a Covid patient, you may get a notification to self-isolate for 14 days when there is no need to do so because you were protected at the time of the contact.

## Temporary Accommodation for Staff reminder

In response to the on-going Covid-19 situation, the Trust will provide alternative accommodation for relevant staff who meet the criteria and are not suspected COVID, but are well, and are either:

- Making the voluntary decision to reside on, or close to the hospital to work additional hours or be on call, and/or
- Making a request to be accommodated close to hospital or away from home due to concerns about family members that they live with (who are either at very high risk of severe illness from Coronavirus (COVID-19) and are being shielded at home, or are symptomatic/have tested positive for Coronavirus and are self-isolating).

**Please remember if you have Covid-19 symptoms, you MUST stay at home and self-isolate. If you do not have symptoms, social distancing is extremely important for you.**

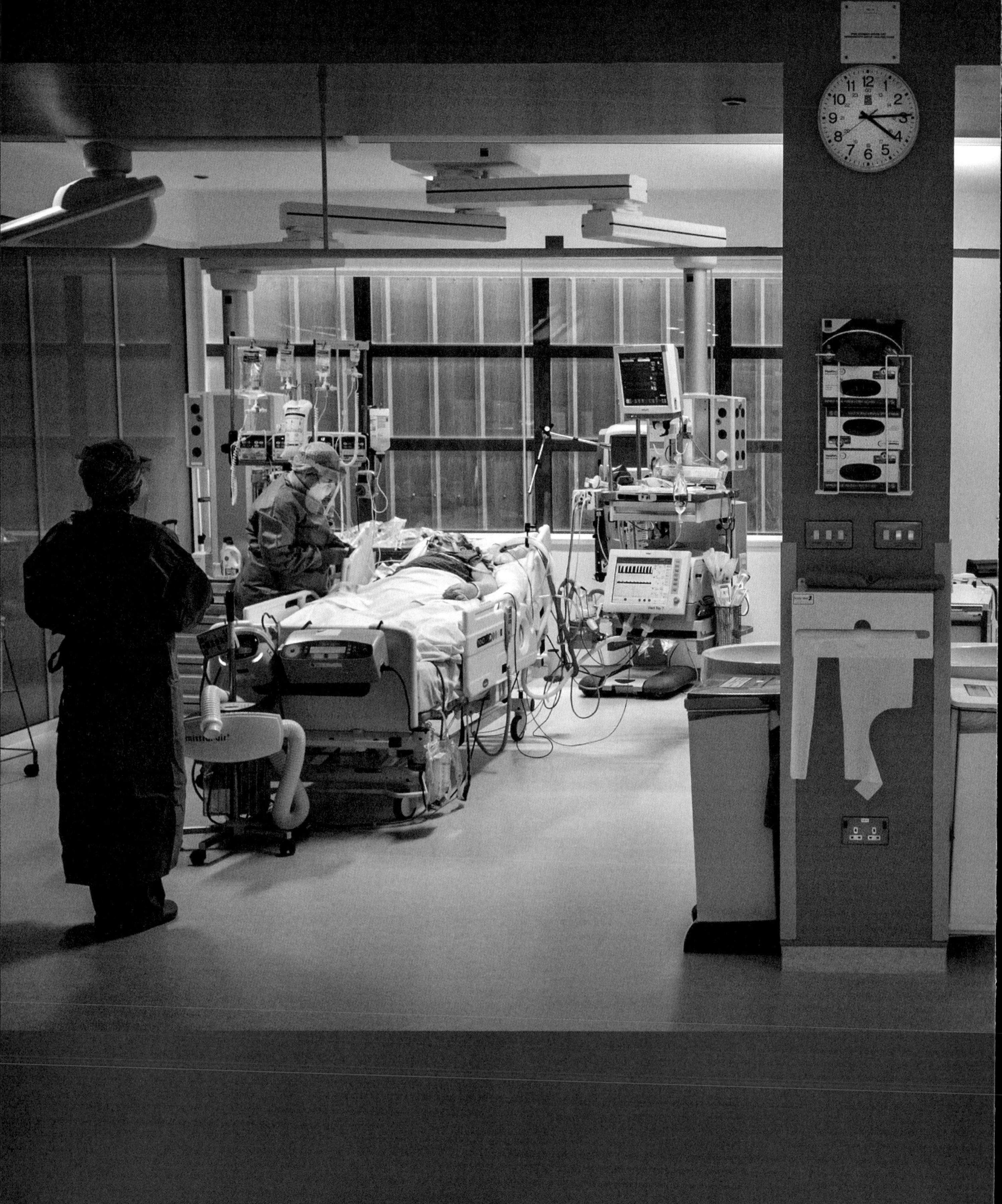

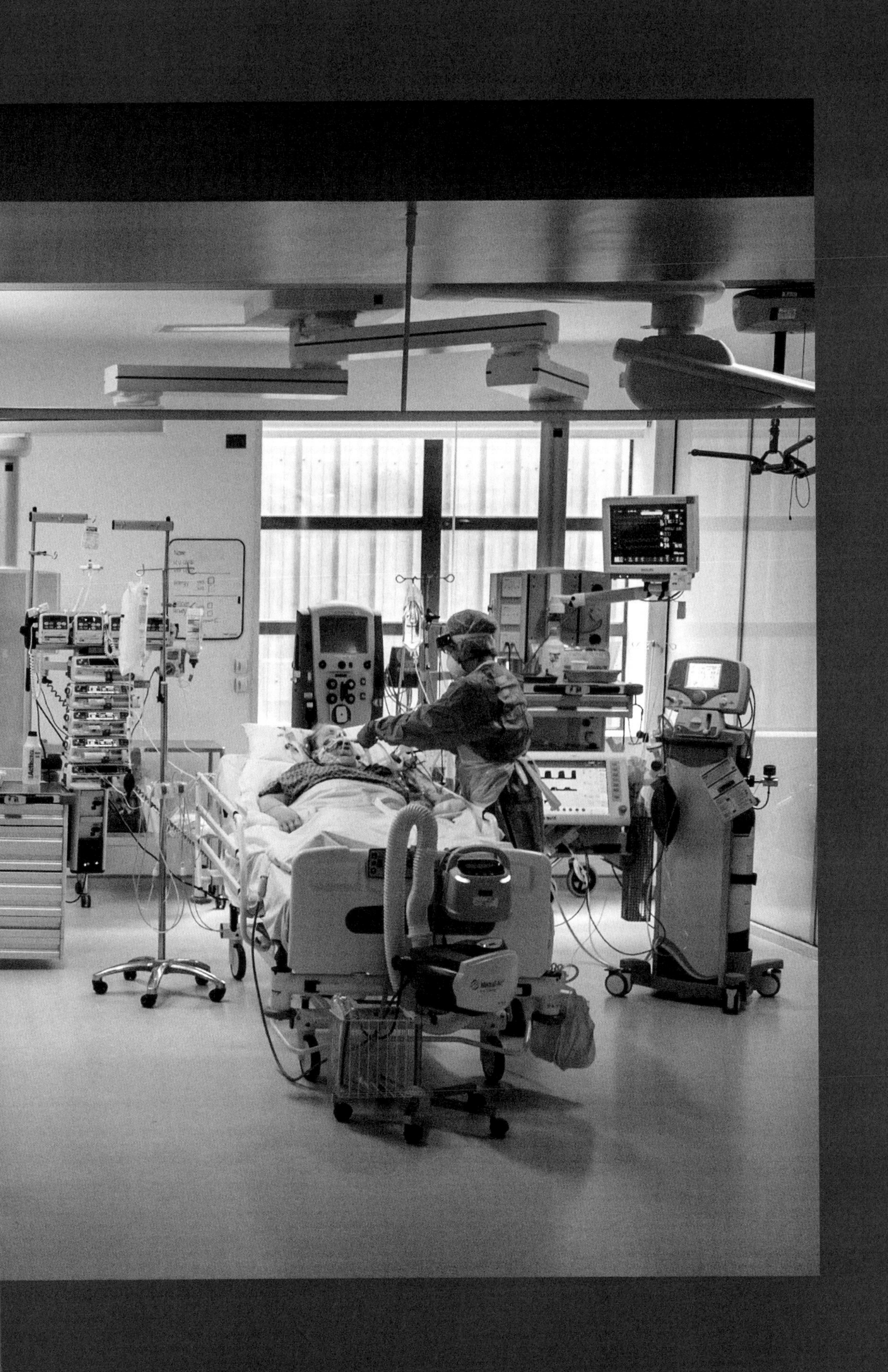

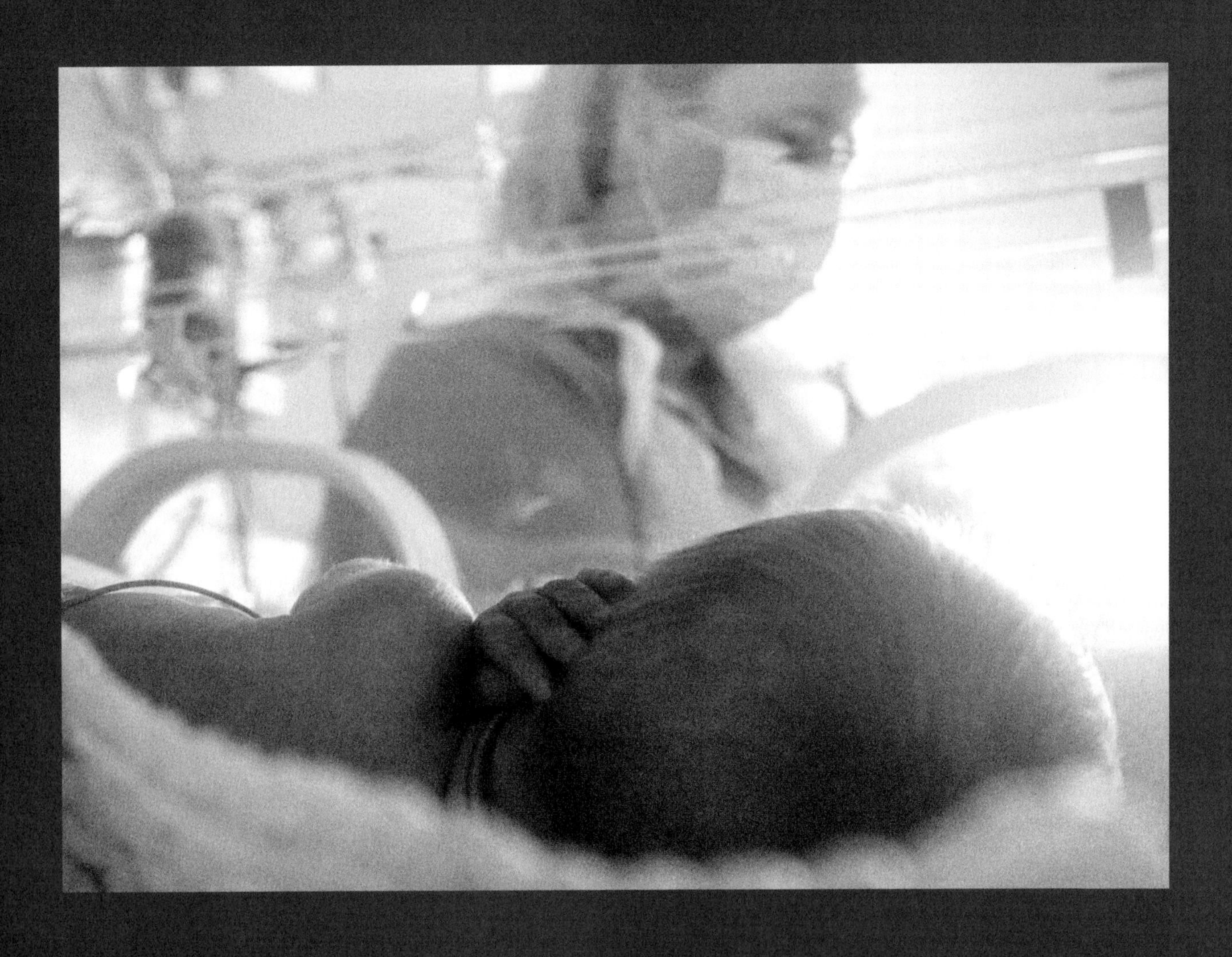

## MENTAL HEALTH

The impact of COVID-19 on our patients, our staff and the service delivery has been far reaching and will likely be long lasting.

Staff from Mental Health Services across the Trust were redeployed in, from and out to other areas and as always, they rose to these new challenges. The pandemic had reduced many of the available referral pathways for our patients and where the staff had to wear PPE, it was found that this hindered rapport and impacted on the overall assessment.

Staff were required to support patients virtually, relying on the therapeutic relationships we develop with them. This only demonstrated how vital the time to build and nurture these relationships was to service delivery and patient outcomes. Our patients responded well to this new way of working, utilising coping skills they had developed and demonstrating resilience during this difficult time.

As we emerge from the pandemic, we face increasing challenges. Addictions, domestic violence, feelings of isolation and loneliness have reached new heights. Attempts to reconnect with vulnerable people are met with record waiting lists. Looking forward, it is hoped that with the implementation of telephone assessments and appointments, this will allow mental health services to be more accessible to those who would have struggled to reach out or engage before.

Hannah Swift
Community Psychiatric Nurse

Alannah Barry
Community Psychiatric Nurse

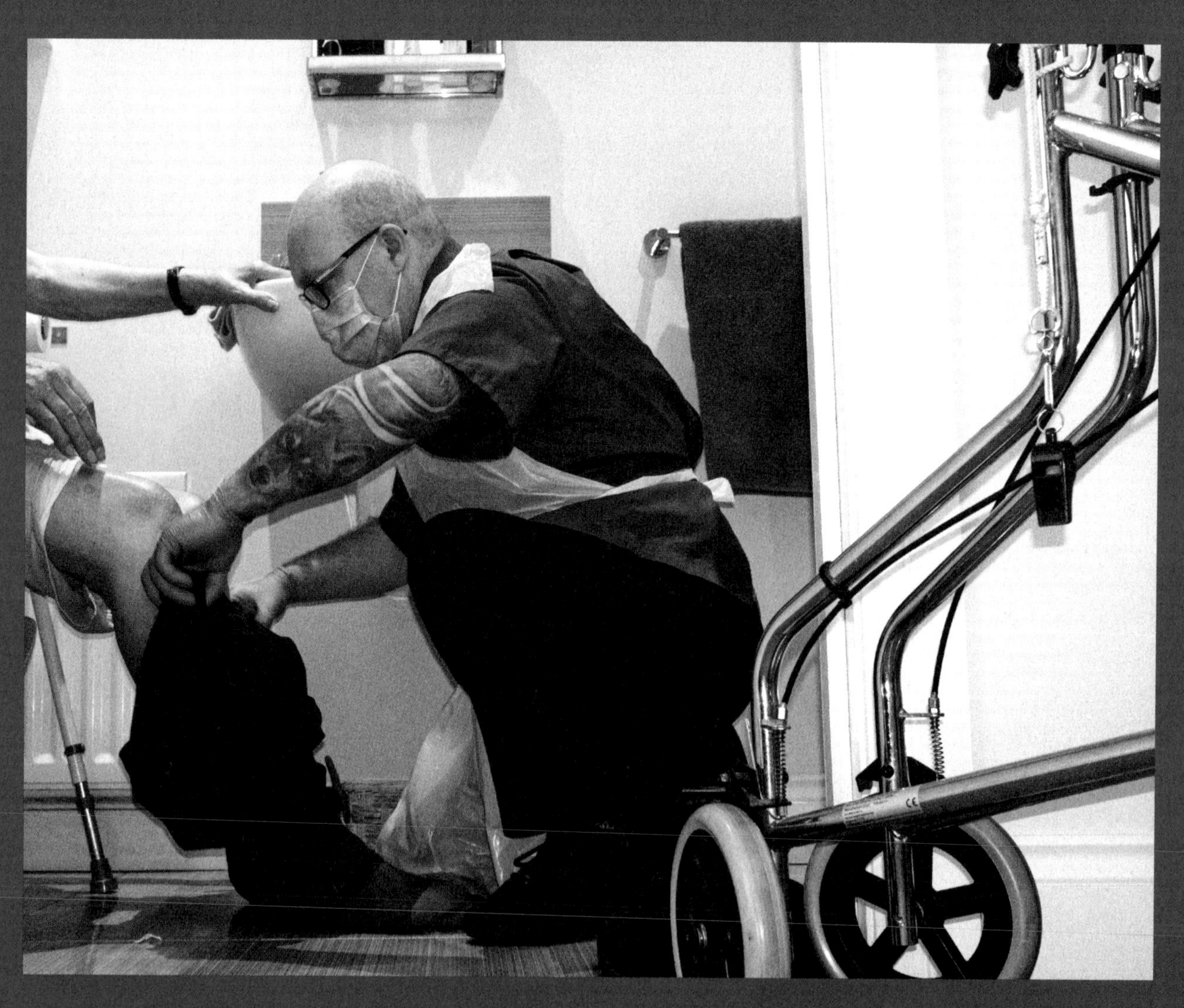

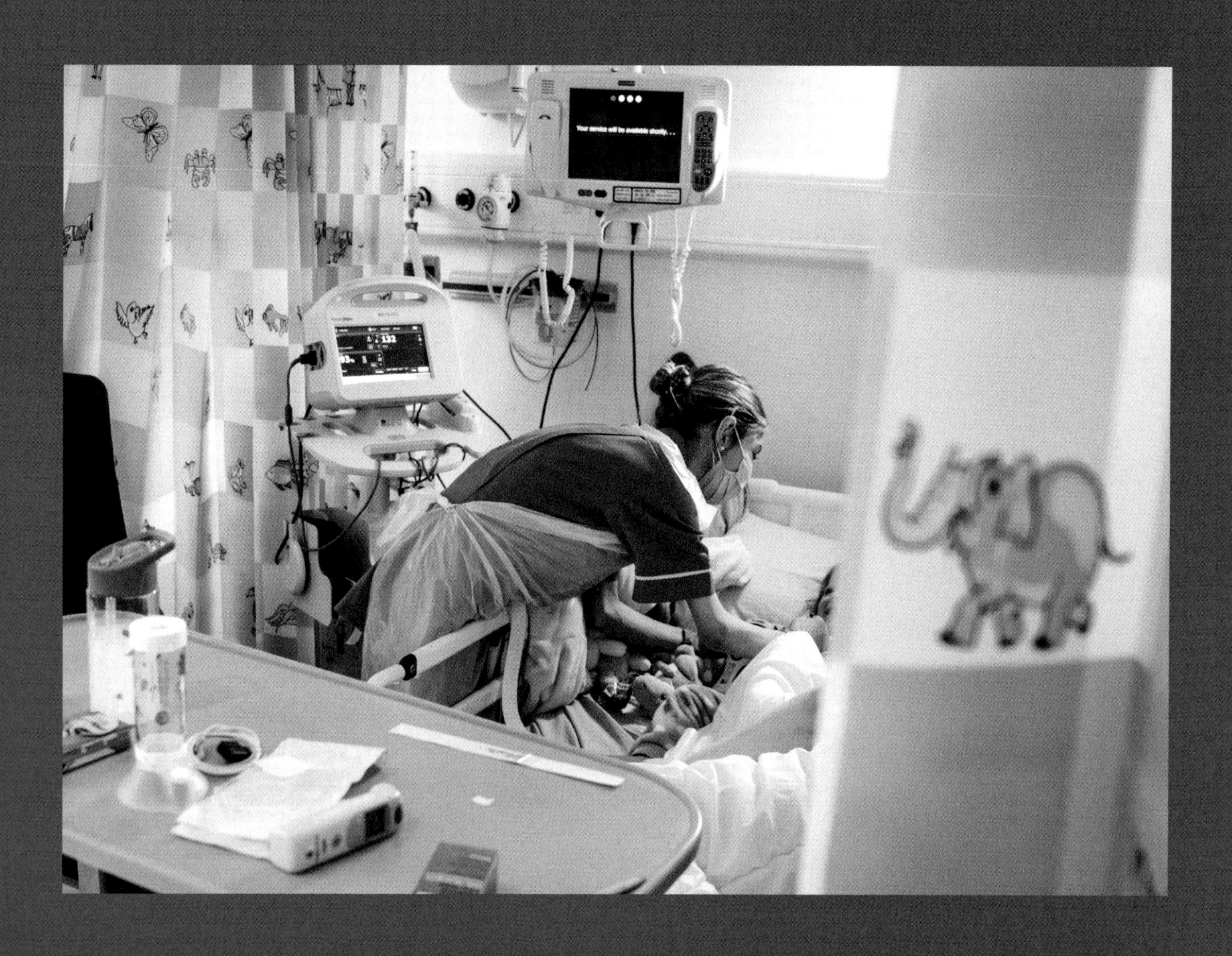

## PAEDIATRICS

On 10 March 2020, Maynard became the Paediatric COVID-19 admission ward. The short few weeks of planning and training beforehand could not prepare us for the reality of this global pandemic that came roaring in out of nowhere.

Emotions ran high and increased levels of anxiety combined with fear dominated as we began to navigate our way through these unprecedented times.

We might all have been in the same storm but we were definitely in different boats. As COVID-19 appeared to be a mild infection in the paediatric population, our patients were being admitted with COVID-19 rather than because of it.

Our initial feelings of immense relief very quickly changed to guilt. This was because we weren't facing the same challenges as our colleagues on the adult side. We used our time wisely and with a positive optimistic attitude, we trained and up-skilled with 'new ways of working' becoming the new normal. Redeployment was however a very real possibility and this 'fish out of water' scenario was yet another source of anxiety and worry.

'Stay home, stay safe' meant we began to see some very unwell children and some parents were too frightened to attend hospital.

Now the reality of the effect of COVID-19 in paediatrics has begun to emerge. The significant increase in the admission of children and young people with behavioural and emotional difficulties brings us new challenges. Nevertheless resilient and undeterred we continue to respond effectively and efficiently to the evolving needs of our patients and their families.

Jill Holland
Deputy Sister

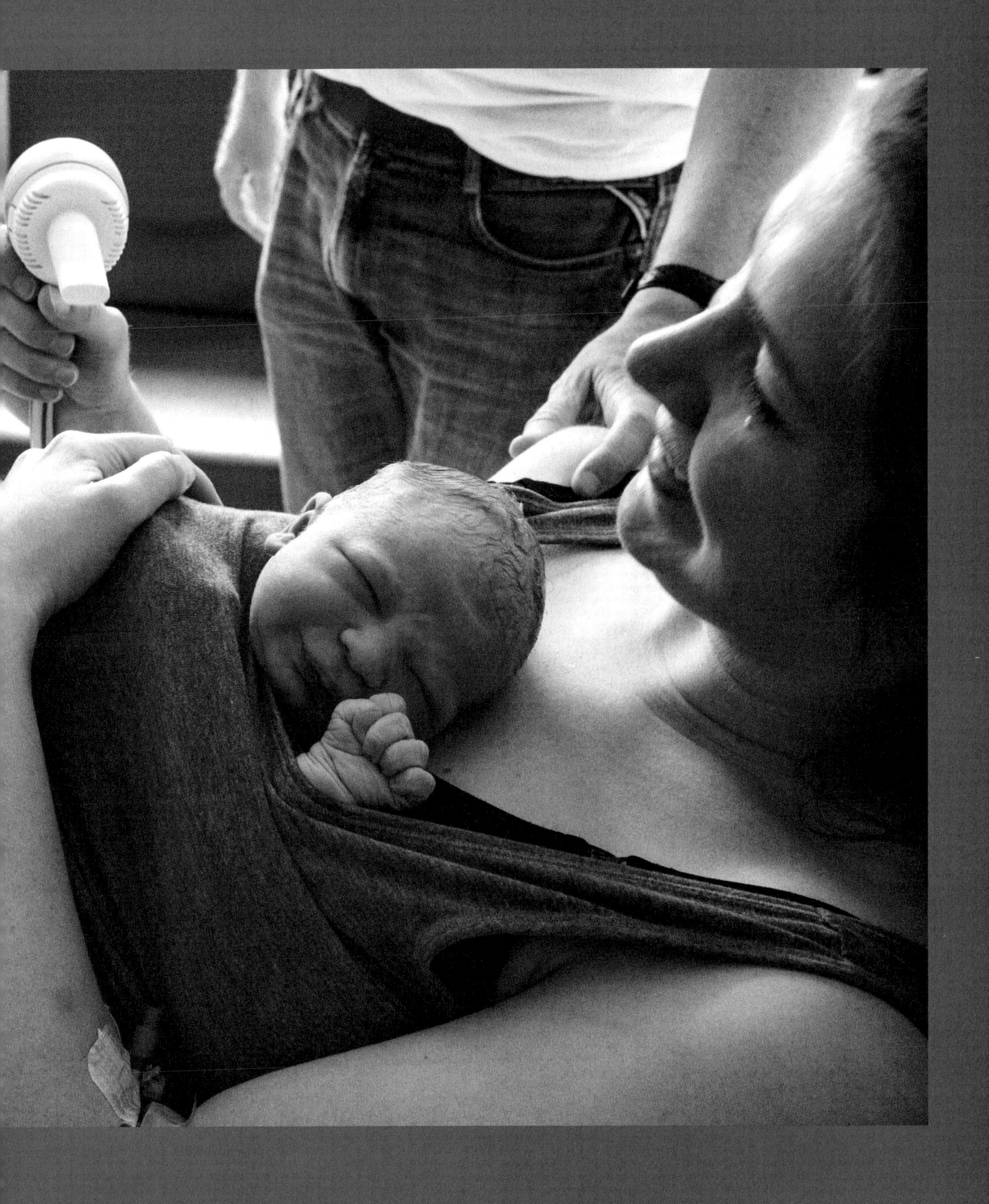

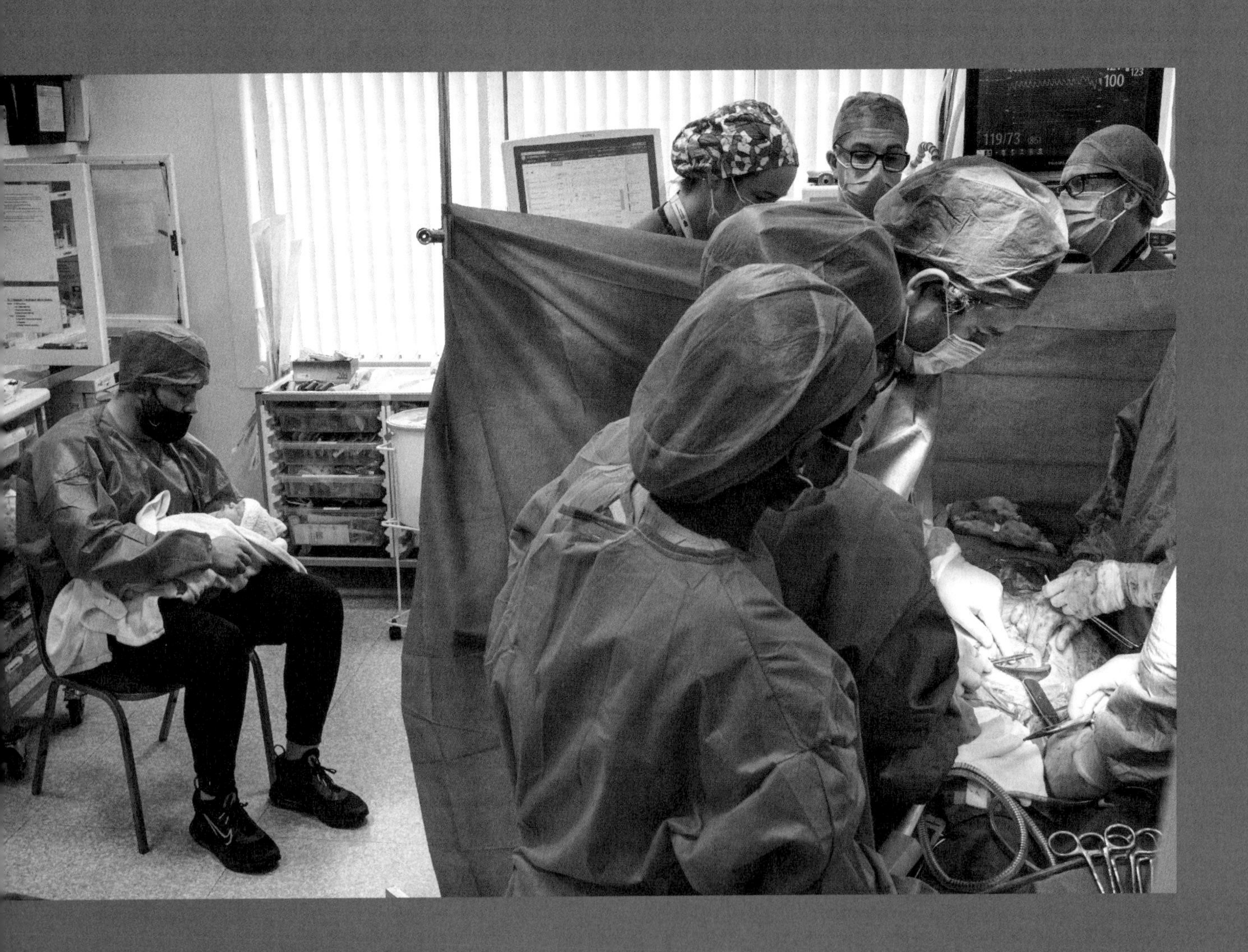
100
119/73

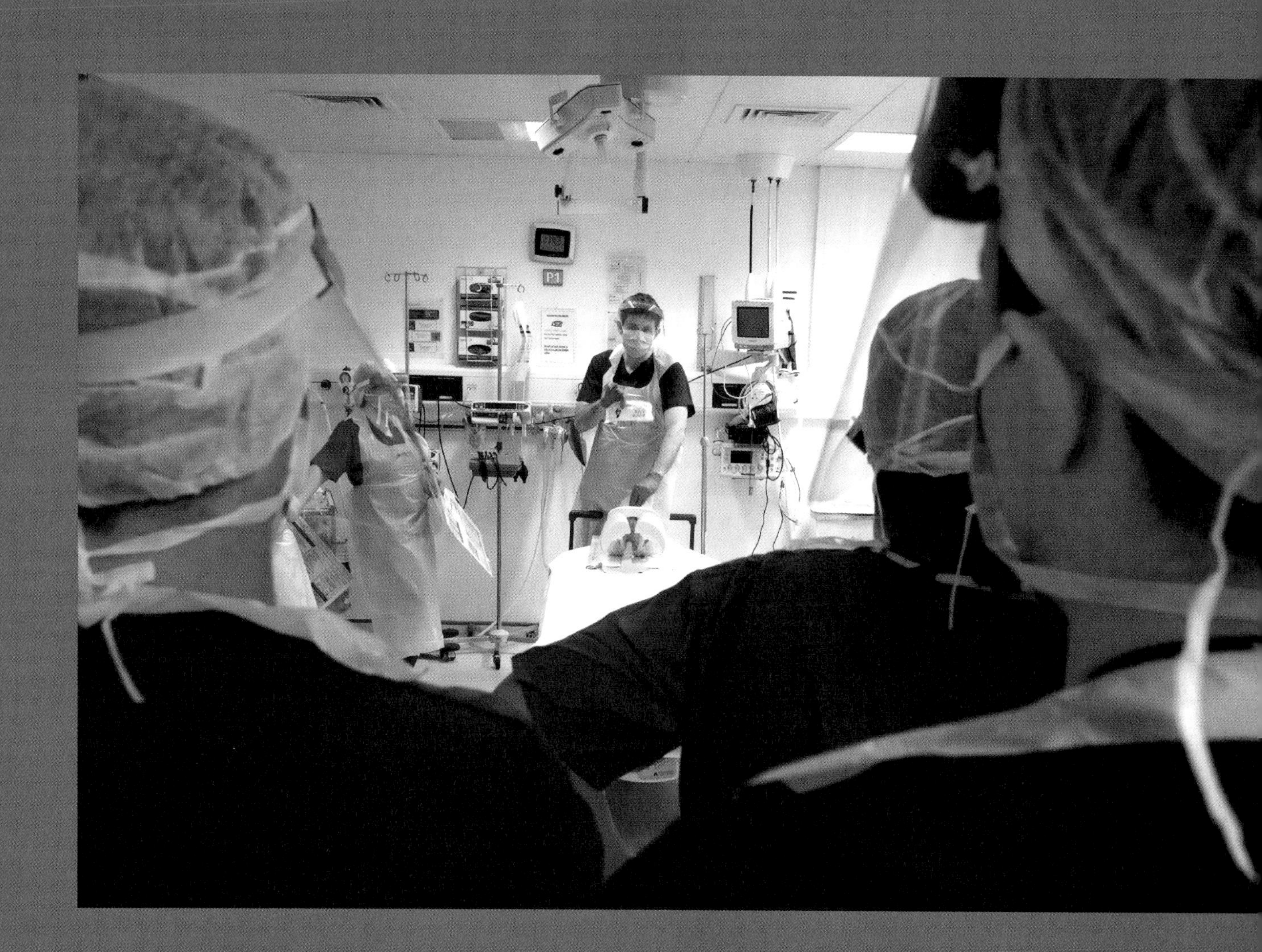
P1

This image still stops me in my tracks. Not only is it powerful but it takes me back to a really painful time in my life. It sums up what so many of us felt during the pandemic - isolation.

During my sepsis recovery, I had another respiratory scare during the middle of the first lockdown. This was my second visit to the Emergency Department of the Ulster Hospital in as many weeks. I was alone and scared.

Illness is a leveller and COVID-19 challenged us all, whether we caught the virus or not. The pandemic has had a profound effect on our families, colleagues, friends and communities.

But our NHS are warriors. I have been treated with care, respect and where appropriate, that inimitable Northern Irish sense of humour.

When reading this book, please remember how far we have come and how resilient we can be when it is our only choice.

Thank you NHS, for your compassion, dedication and care.

Rebecca McKinney
Patient

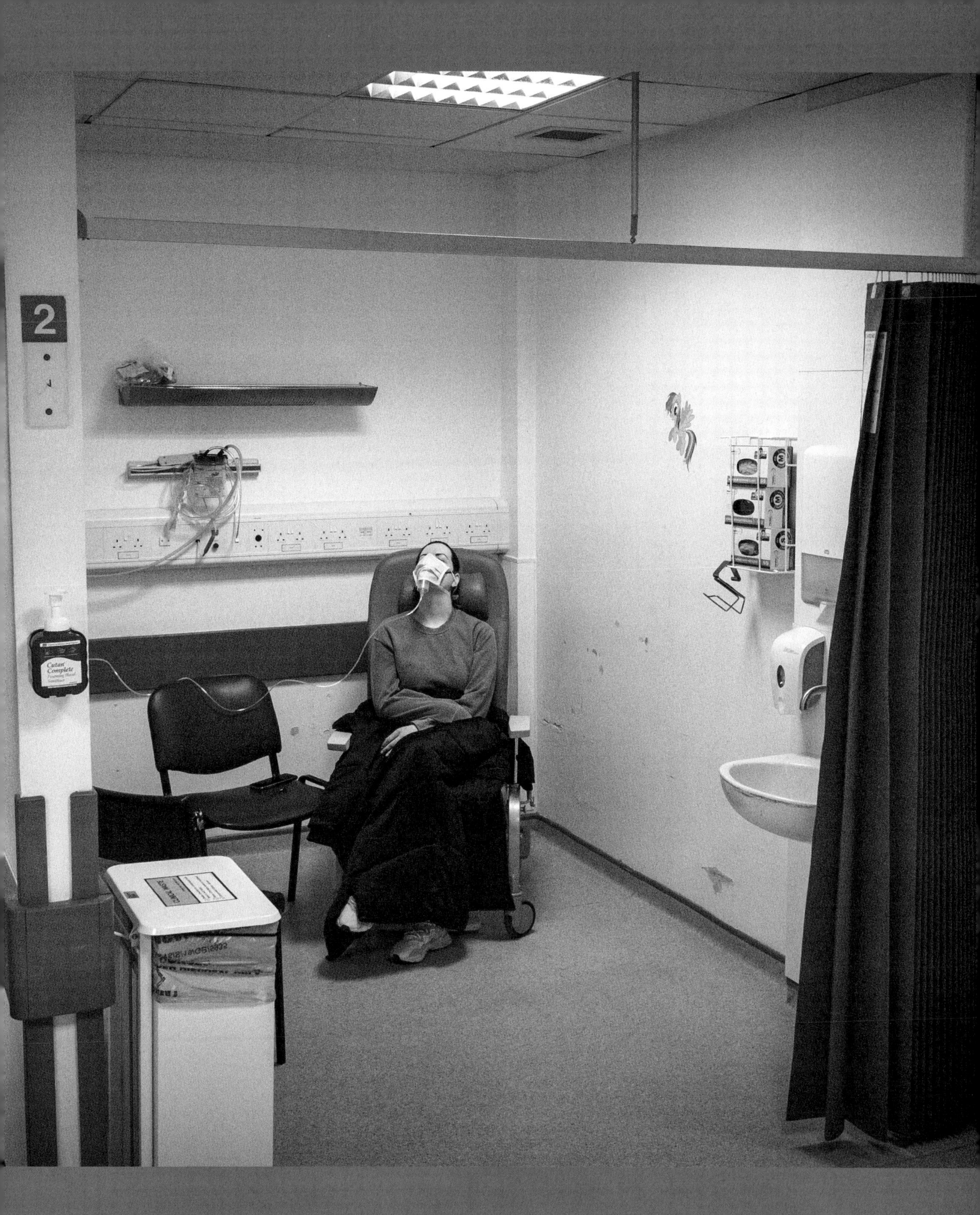
2
Cutan
Complete

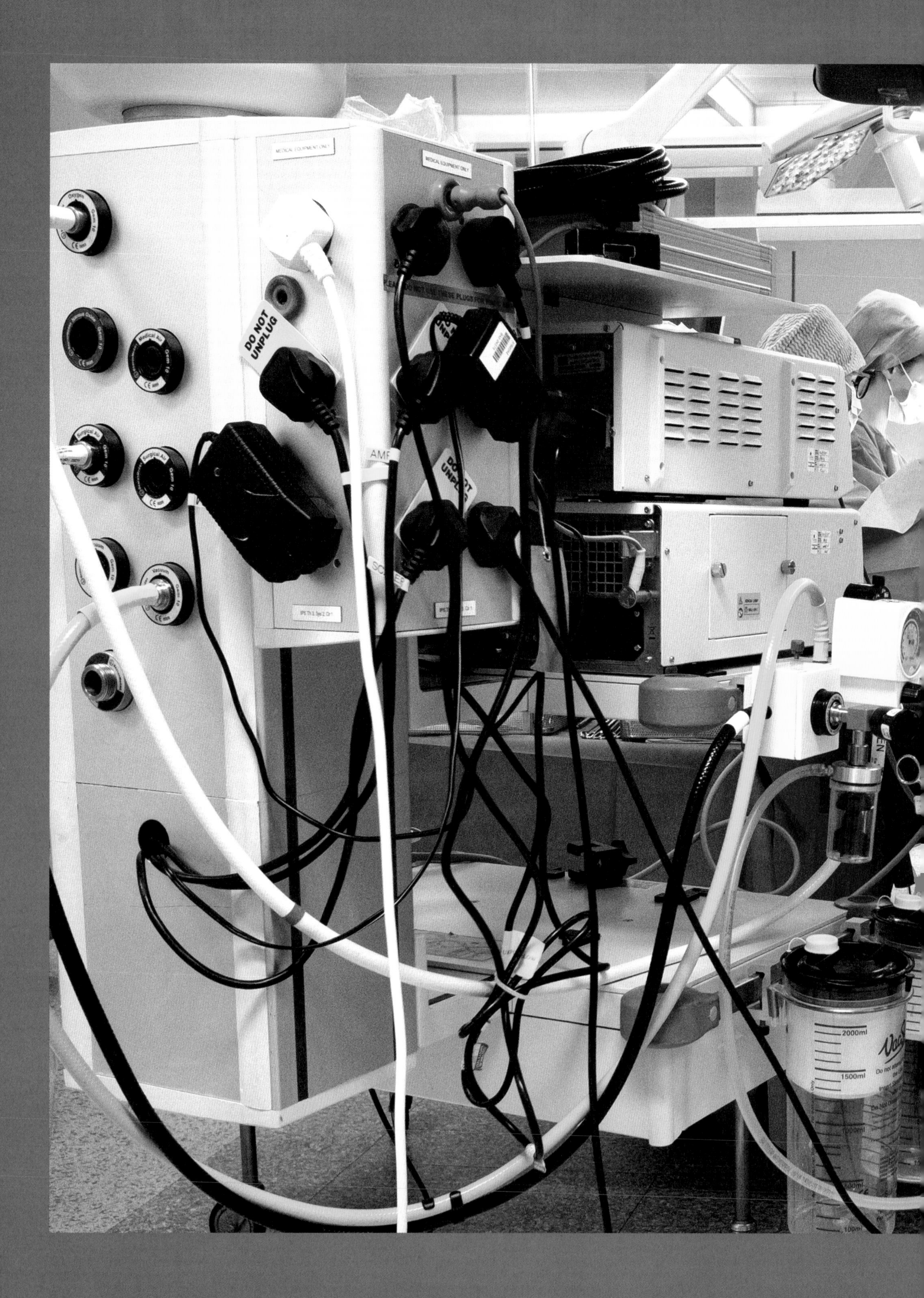

DO NOT UNPLUG
Medical Air
Surgical Air
2000ml
1500ml
1000ml

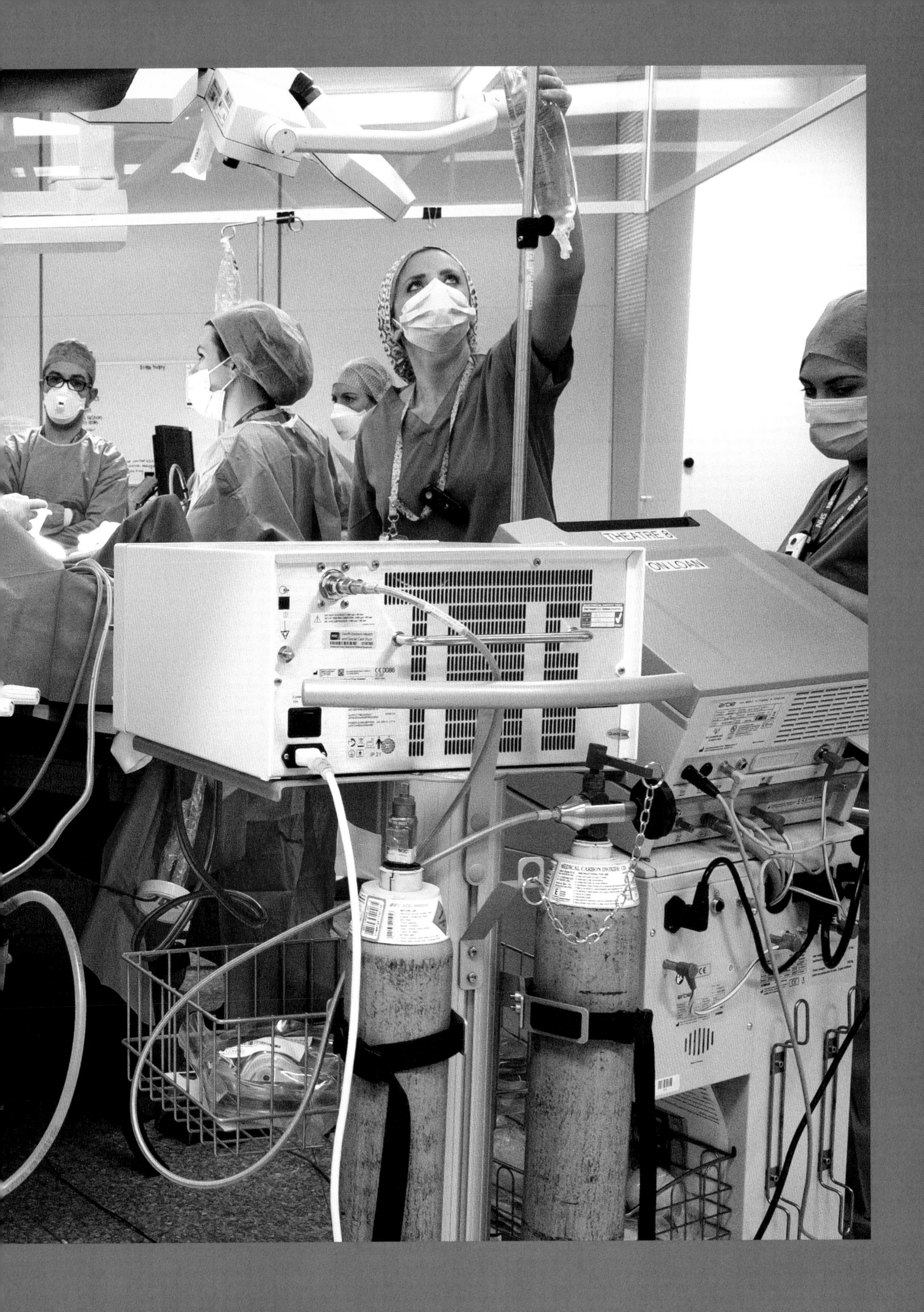
THEATRE 8
ON LOAN
MEDICAL CARBON DIOXIDE

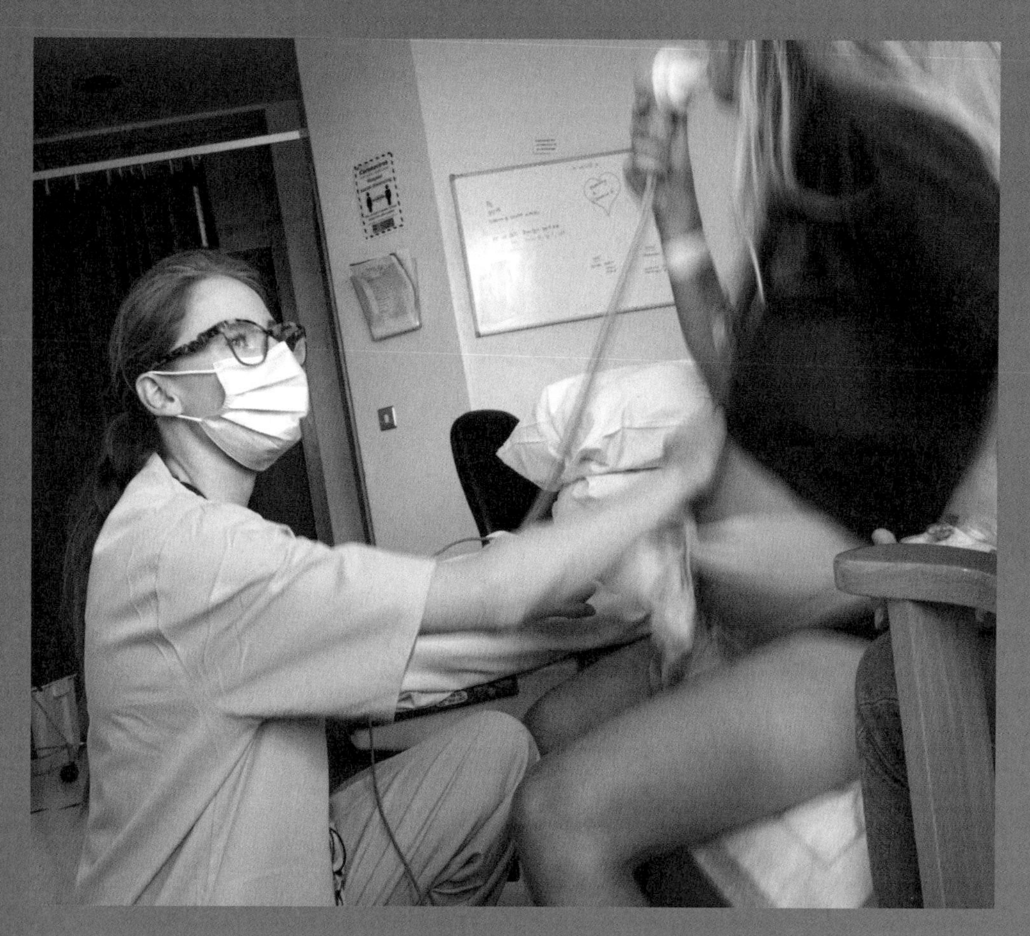

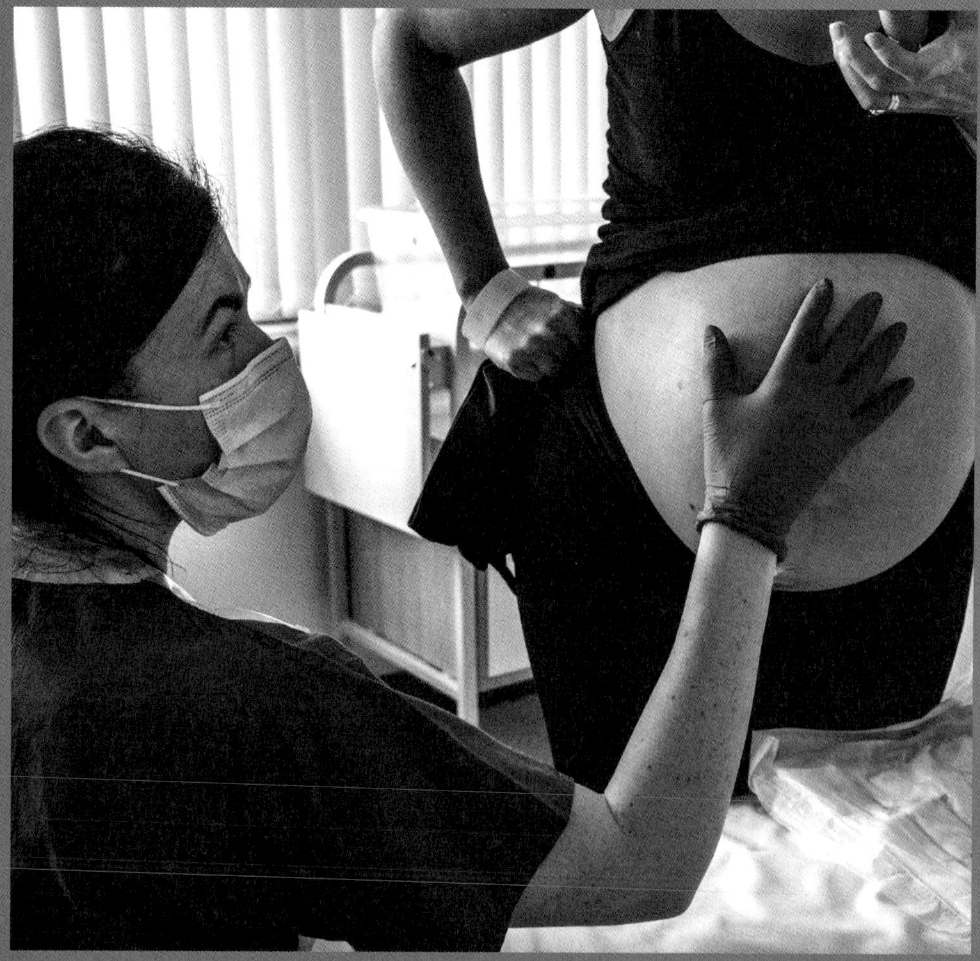

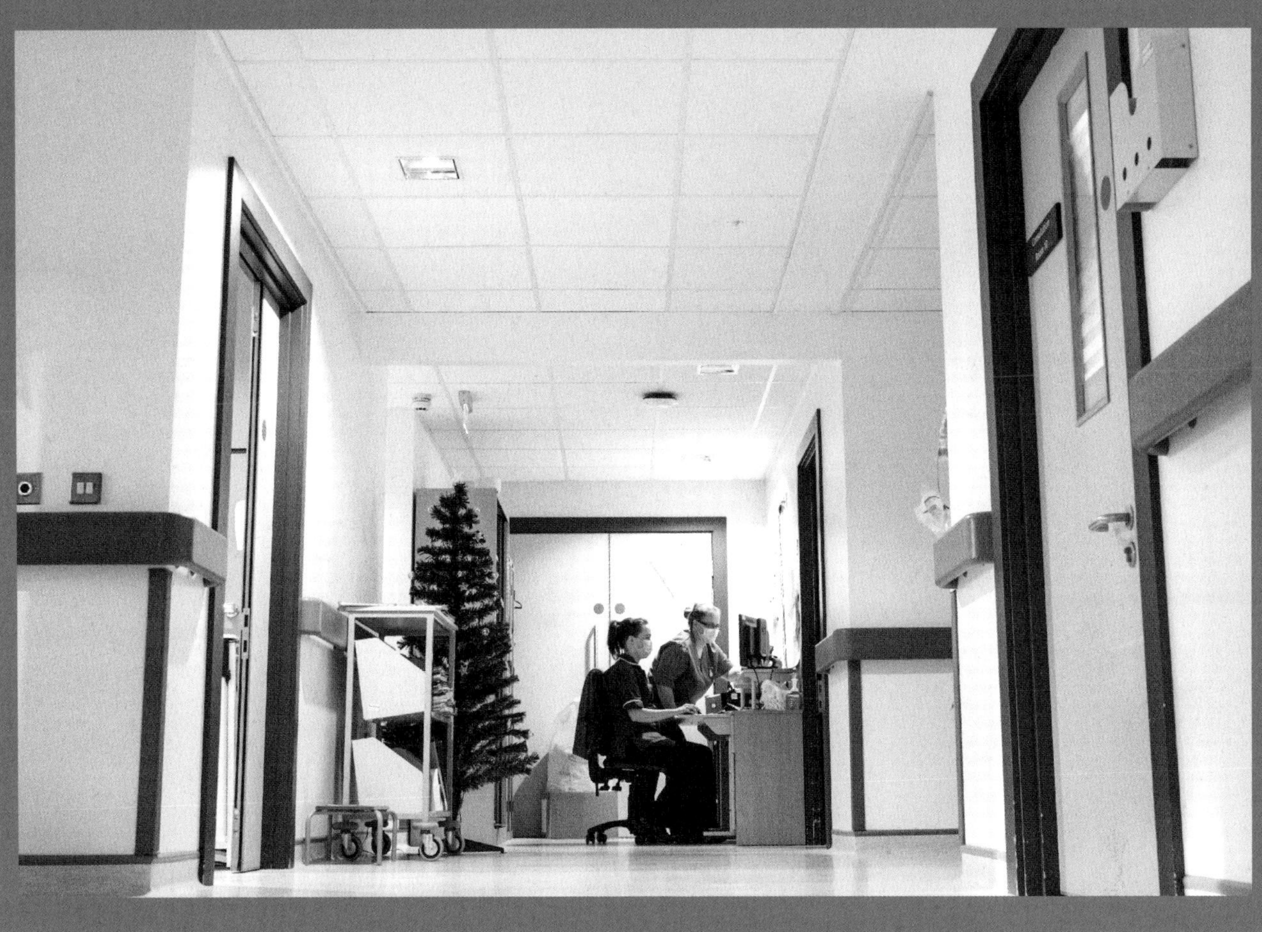

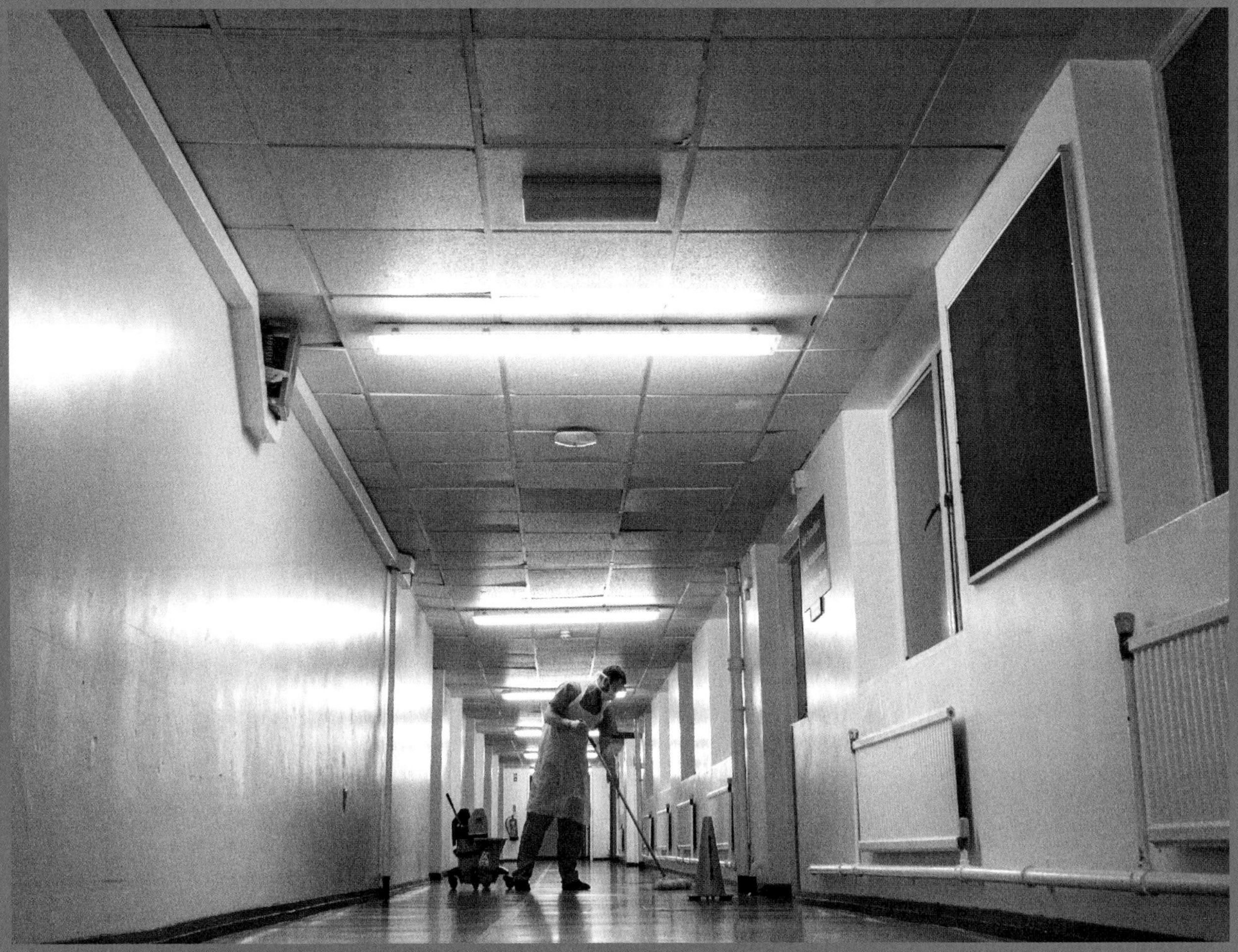

16
Maximum Occupancy
for this room
2
If social distancing (2m) cannot
be adhered to,
wear appropriate PPE

## EASTER 2020. THE LONG CORRIDOR

Paul McGouran, Radiographer

I have met them at the end of shift
coming with tired faces
from ward or office.
I have passed them with a nod of the head
and a polite meaningful smile.

Receiving back a nod of the head
and a polite meaningful smile.
This nurse has been worried sick all day.
Her parents are seven thousand miles away
with no daughter to look out for them.
This junior doctor suffers from panic attacks.
Yet today she breathed compassion
into the air of a dozen COVID isolation rooms.
The love in her eyes deep enough
to see the value of each patient's life.
This cleaner never imagined
That she would be on the frontline.
In this battle with the virus
she is in the forward trenches.
This nursing assistant is dead on his feet.
He has just finished a twelve-hour shift
his fifth this week.
This porter chats so easily to the patient in his chair.
Tonight, he will go home to a loved one
whose chemo has been postponed.
This manager's head is still spinning
from a day of endless meetings.
It will be the small hours of the morning
before her pulse rests.
This consultant is doing his best
trying to lead from the front.
He is tired now
after spending long hours in full PPE.

So, what is this that has visited our hospital?
Is it fear, suffering, despair and death?
Yes, and don't try to sanitise it!
But it is more, much more.
We have been visited by love, kindness
gentleness and self-sacrifice.
And best of all, we have been visited by
the sometimes subtle joy of recovery.
At the end of the day
this is what we all strive for.

ONLY 1 PATIENT / STAFF
MEMBER AT ONE TIME
PLEASE WAIT IN CORRIDOR UNTIL
ROOM IS FREE

Aciclovir

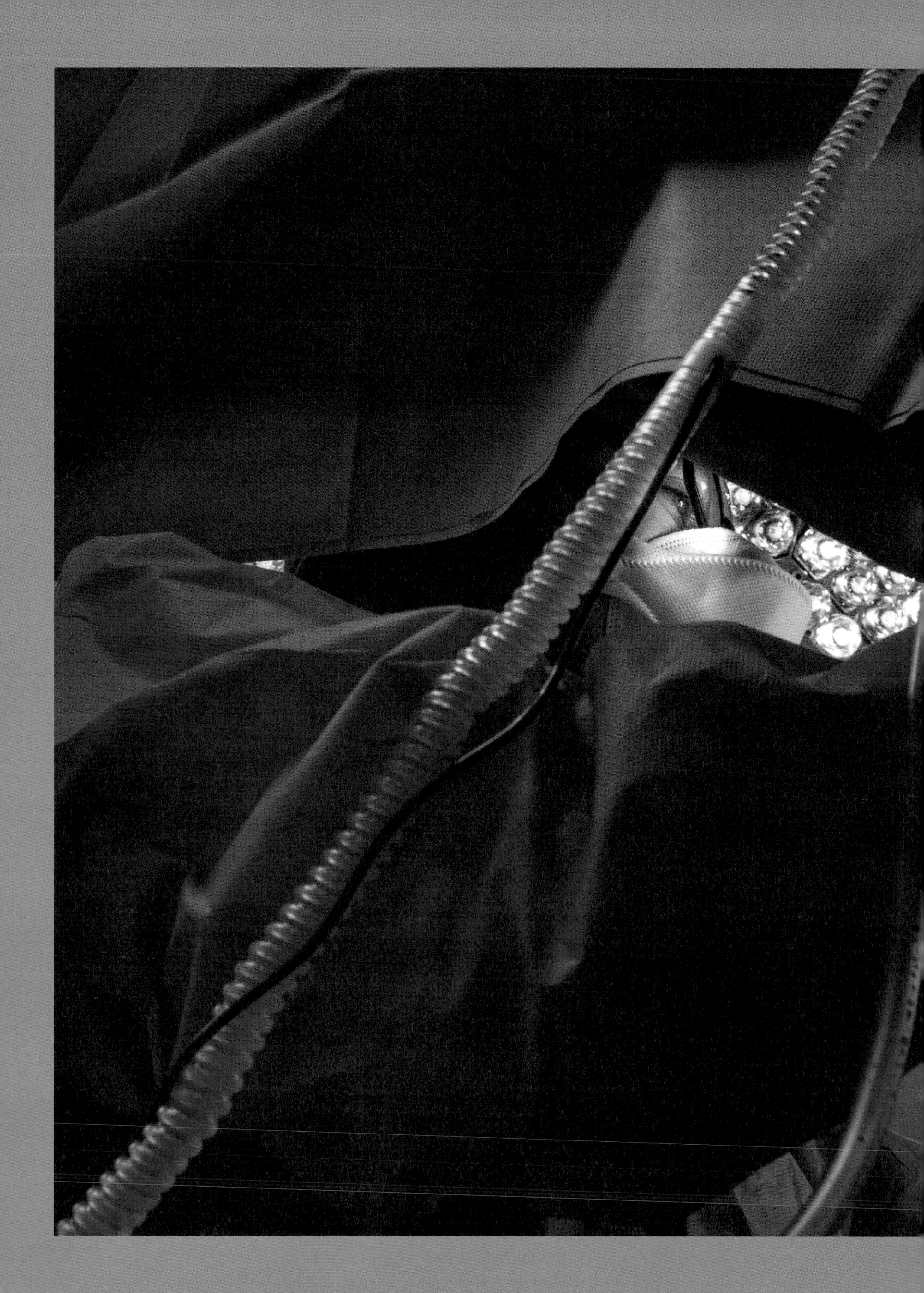

To all our colleagues who lost their lives

We are eternally grateful for your dedication, service and sacrifice

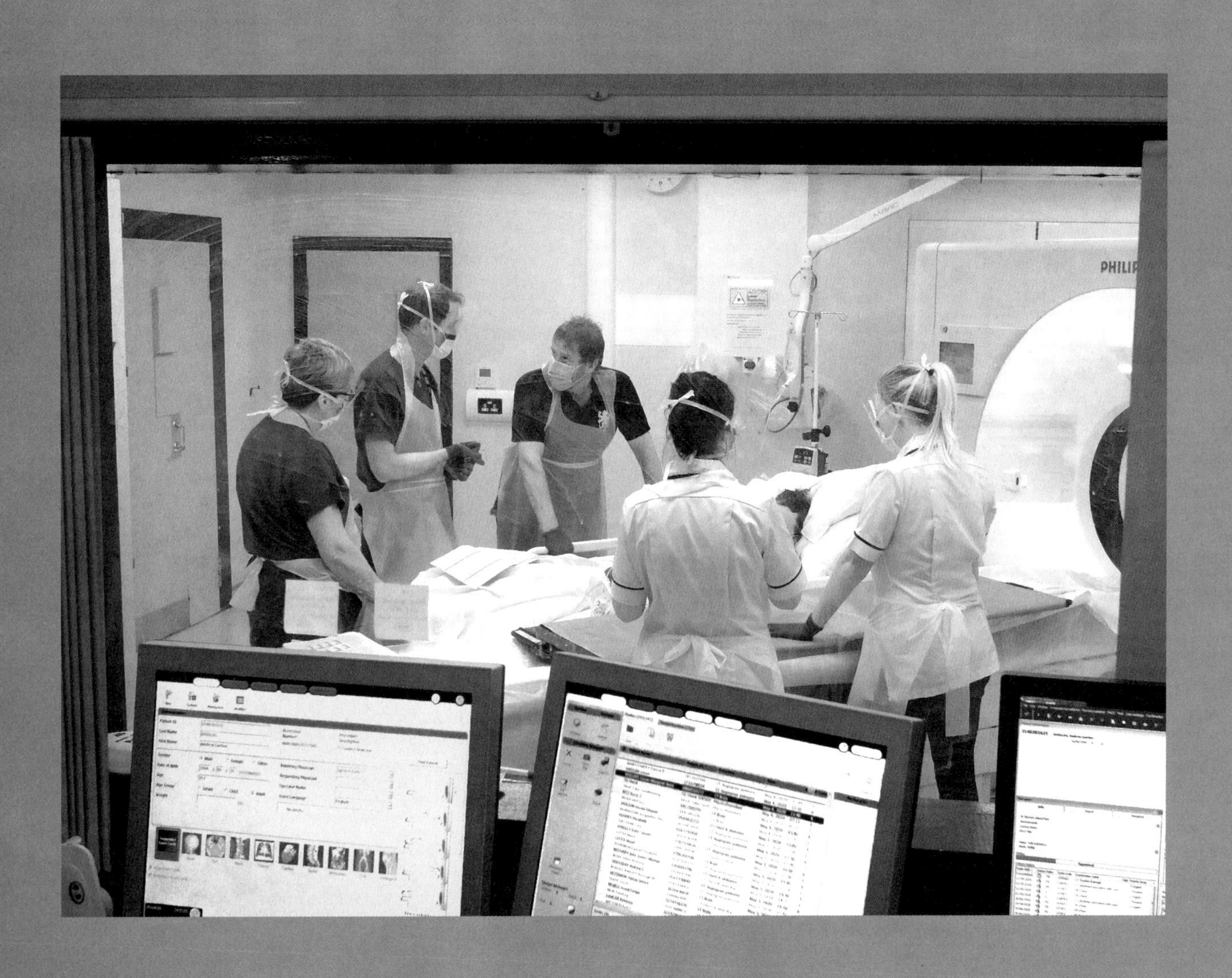

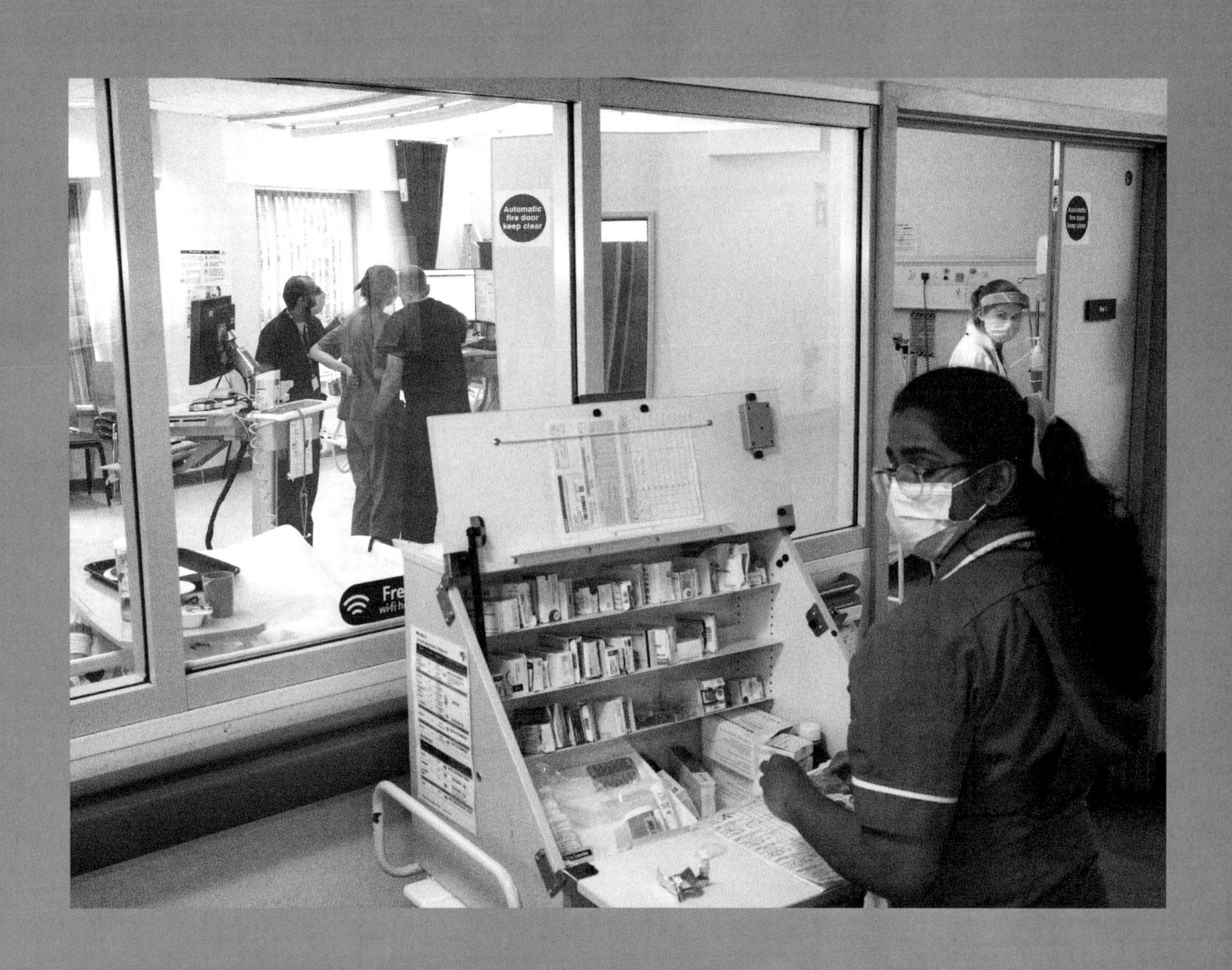
Automatic
fire door
keep clear

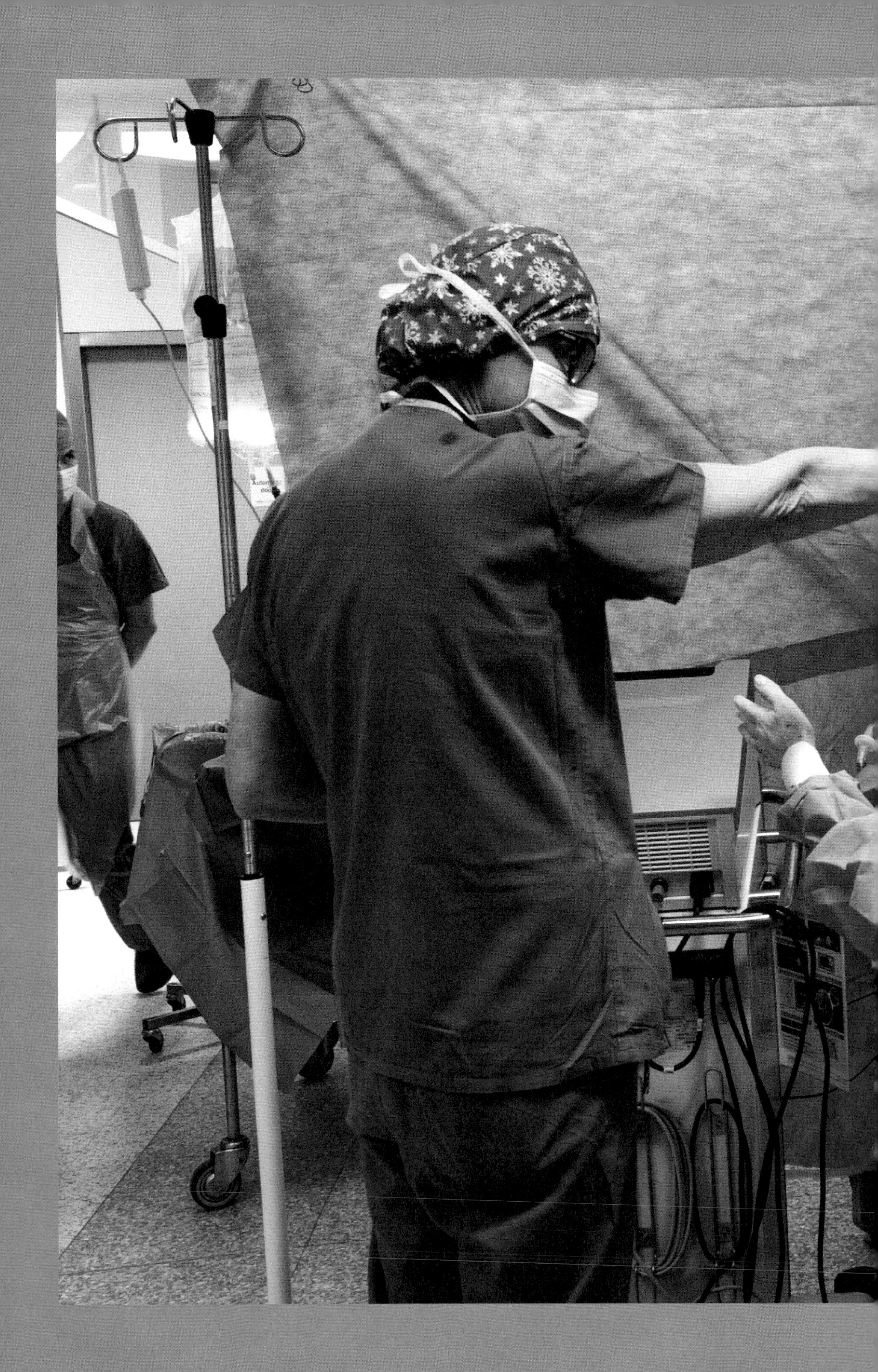

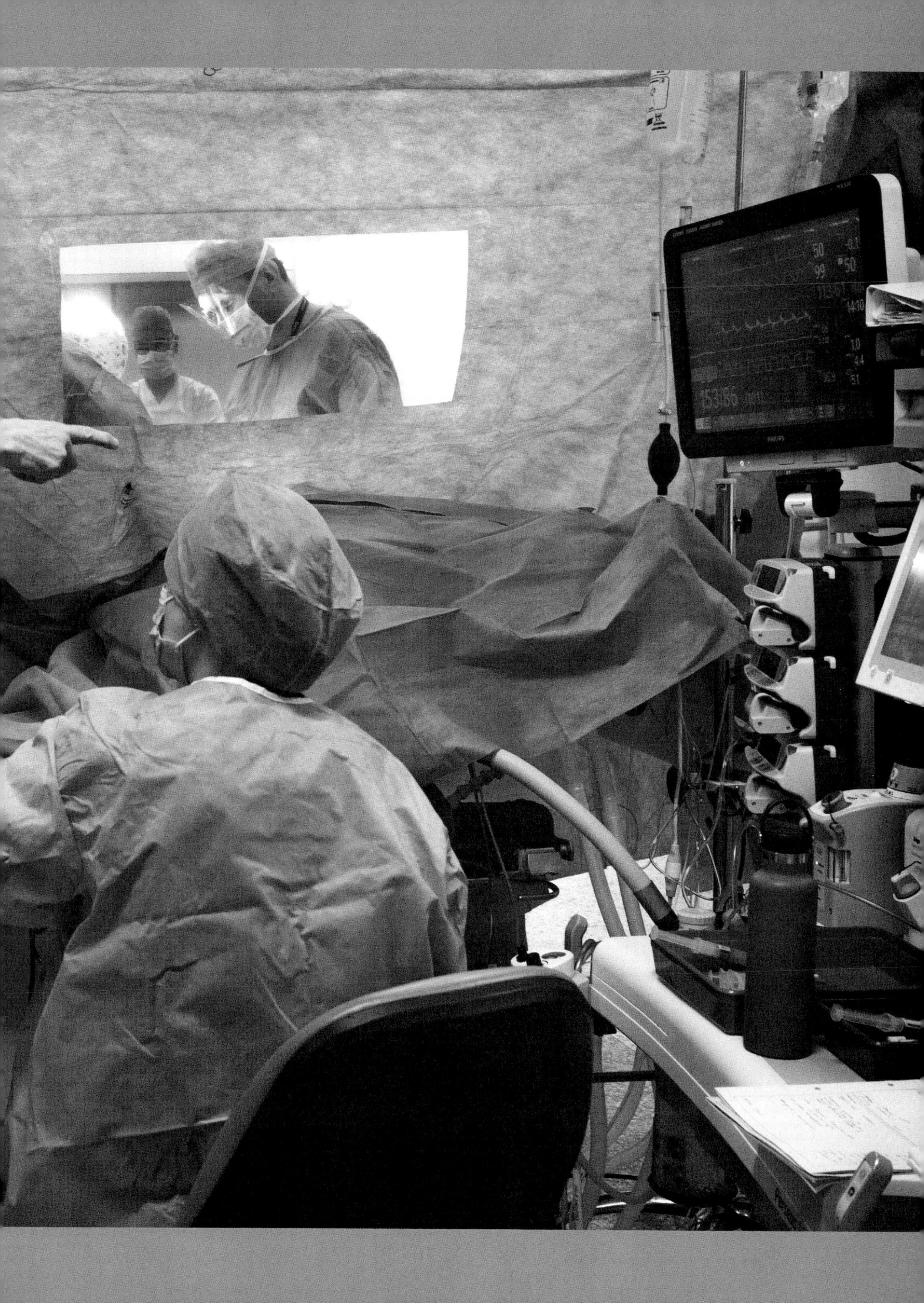

## LAUNDRY

Restructuring of working patterns in the department proved essential in providing a safe environment for our operators while also facilitating the exponential demands on our service. These issues although frustrating were within our control and as with most areas of health care, we simply adapted and carried on.

The constant disruptions to global supply chains proved to be a slightly more difficult problem as this was completely outside of our control, but with necessity being the mother of invention, the PPE shortages created opportunities for a long-term conversion to reusable isolation gowns providing a cost effective, sustainable alternative to the problematic disposables.

Robust healthcare hygiene standards already in place meant there wasn't any major need for change in laundry processes but there were significant changes in both volume and classification.

There was a marked increase of deliveries of scrubs and soluble laundry bags. Infected processes soared to almost 70% of overall production during the first and second waves of the virus, predominantly scrub suits, but with visitation access restricted, hospital gowns had become standard bed wear for all patients.

Andrew Stevenson
Service Manager

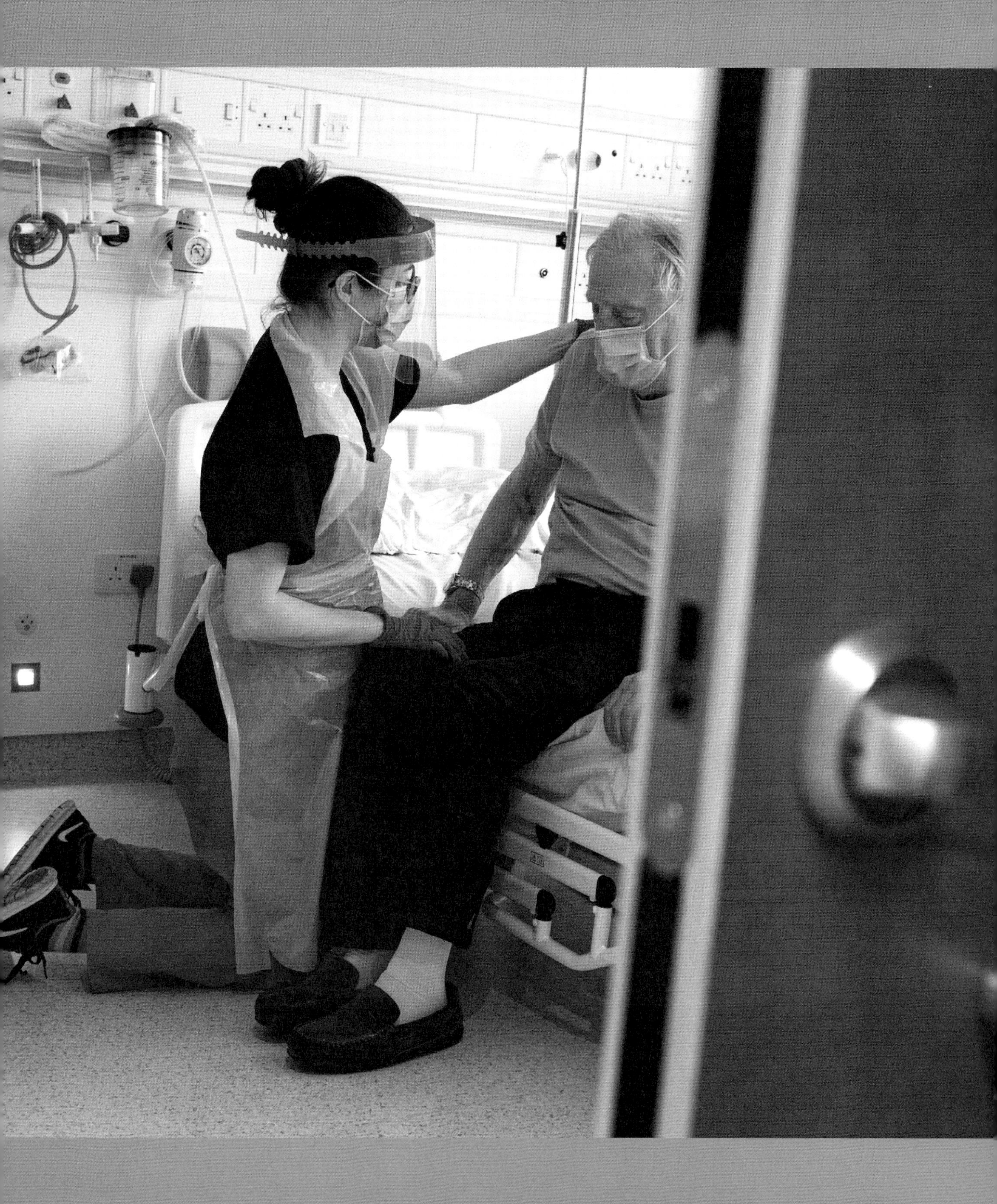

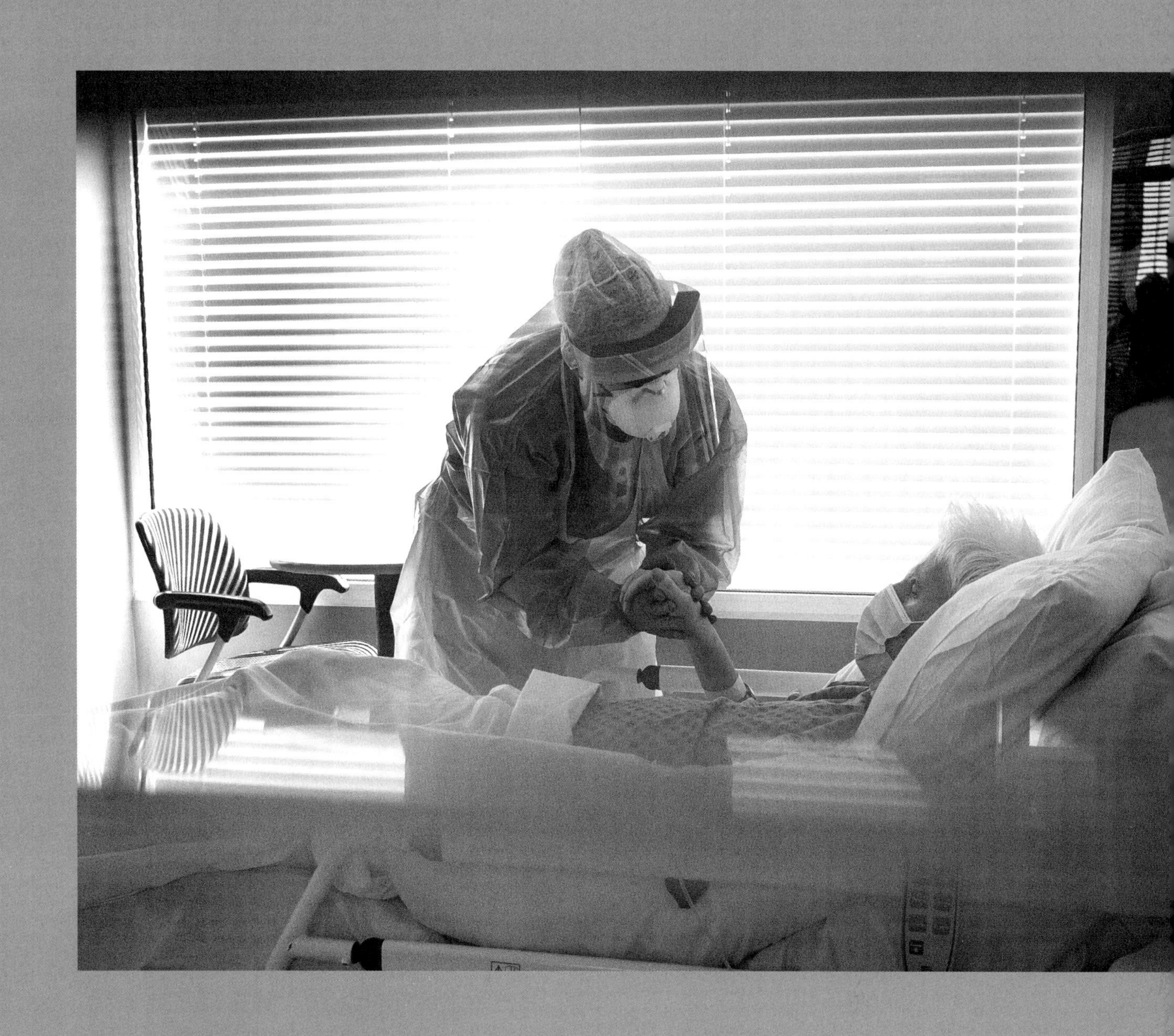

GAMBRO

Main Entrance
PATU

## MATERNITY

The pandemic has overwhelmed us all, both in our home and working lives. No one knew what to expect, our days and nights on labour ward were faced with constant uncertainties. We turned up, changed into our scrubs, and became accustomed to our 'new' ways. We worked alongside new standard operating procedures, became flexible with guidance that changed daily, and supported our service users in all that they needed. We continued to 'set the bar high' and achieve the standard of care that only we would accept ourselves.

Our SEHSCT maternity unit doors have remained open, and our team have been present each day to support, care and be there to bring new life into the world. We care for families during one of the most vulnerable and life altering times; a complete privilege.

The COVID-19 pandemic has affected maternity services in a variety of ways and midwives and obstetricians have adapted while maintaining a normal service. One of the most impactful changes relates to the use of PPE. Our non-verbal communication skills are there to reassure and encourage women, especially throughout labour. This has become even more important with the use of PPE. Midwives, obstetricians and healthcare assistants within maternity, now rely on talking with our eyes, now more than ever!

From the beginning of the pandemic in March 2020 to March 2022, we are proud to say we have safely delivered approximately 8,000 births on our unit.

Emma Johnson
Acting Ward Manager

AMBULANCE

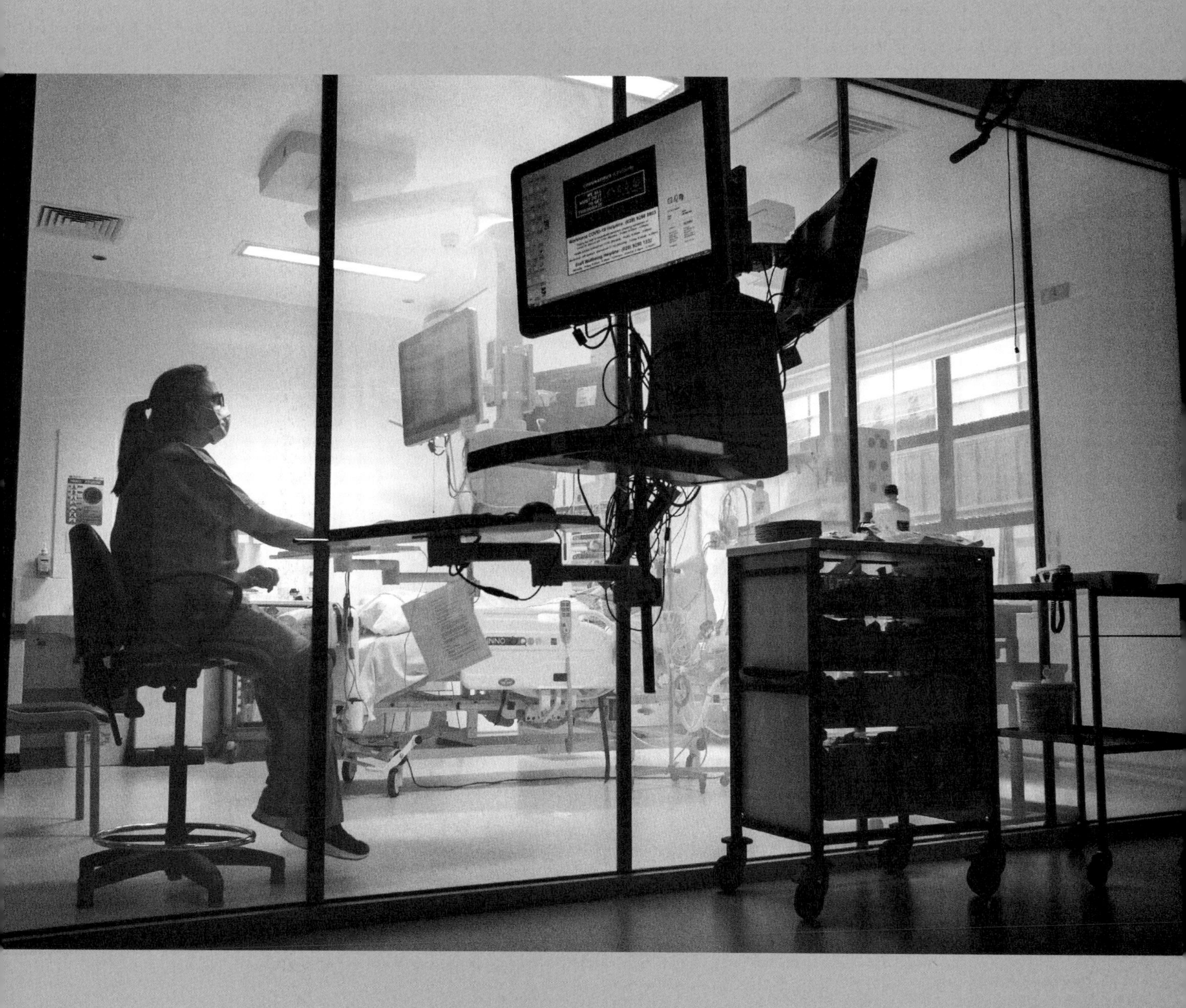

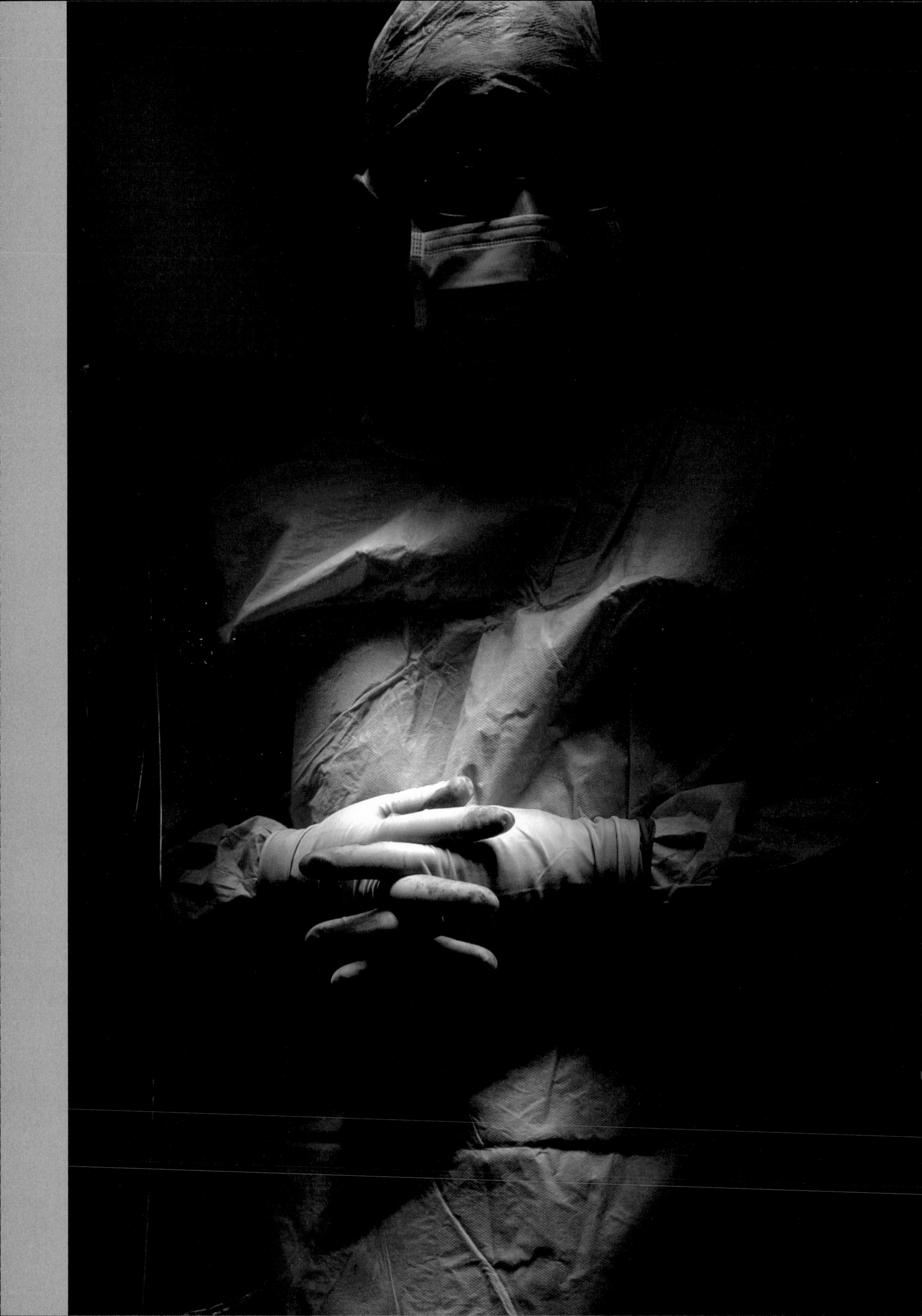

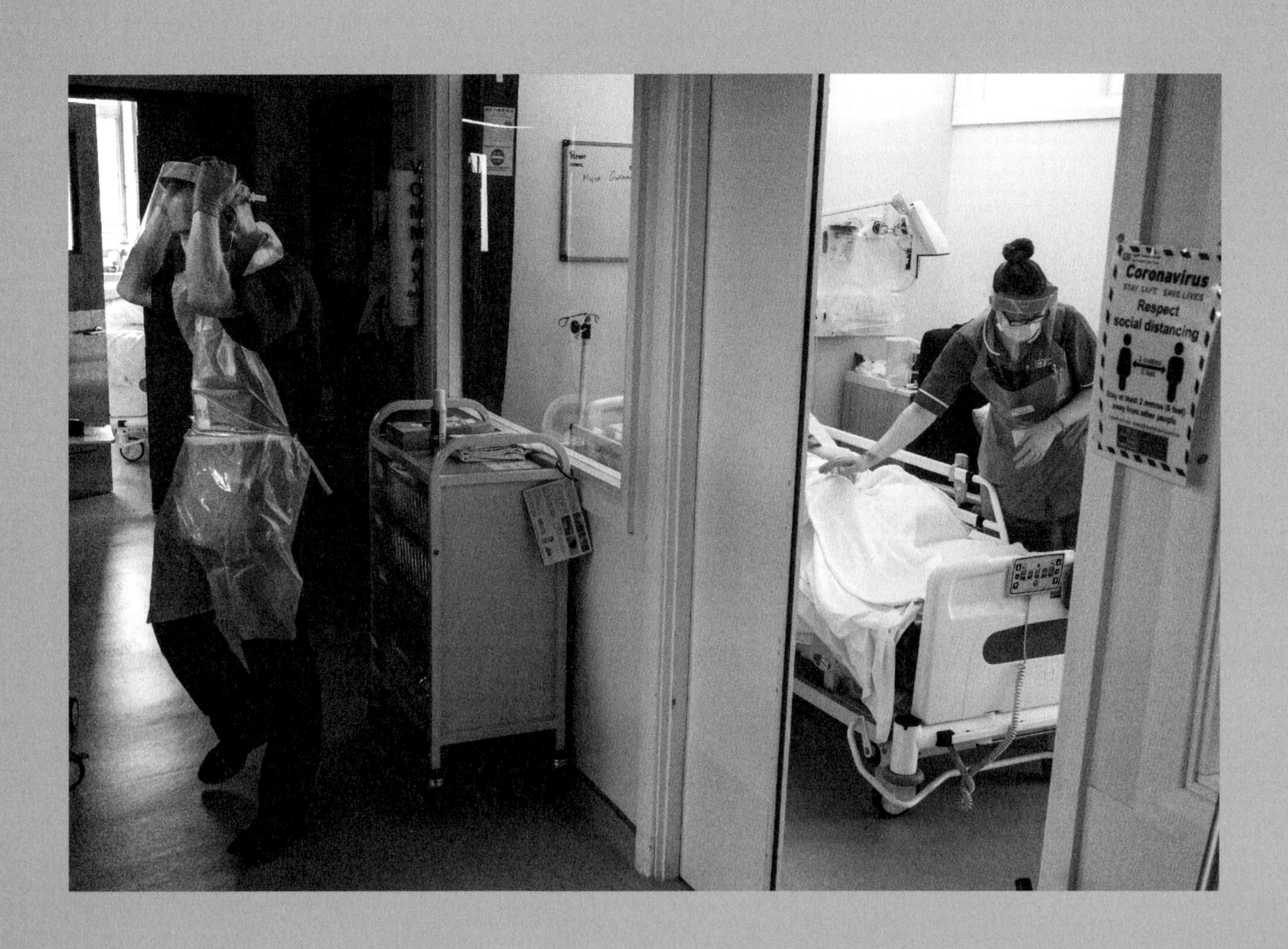
Coronavirus
STAY SAFE SAVE LIVES
Respect
social distancing

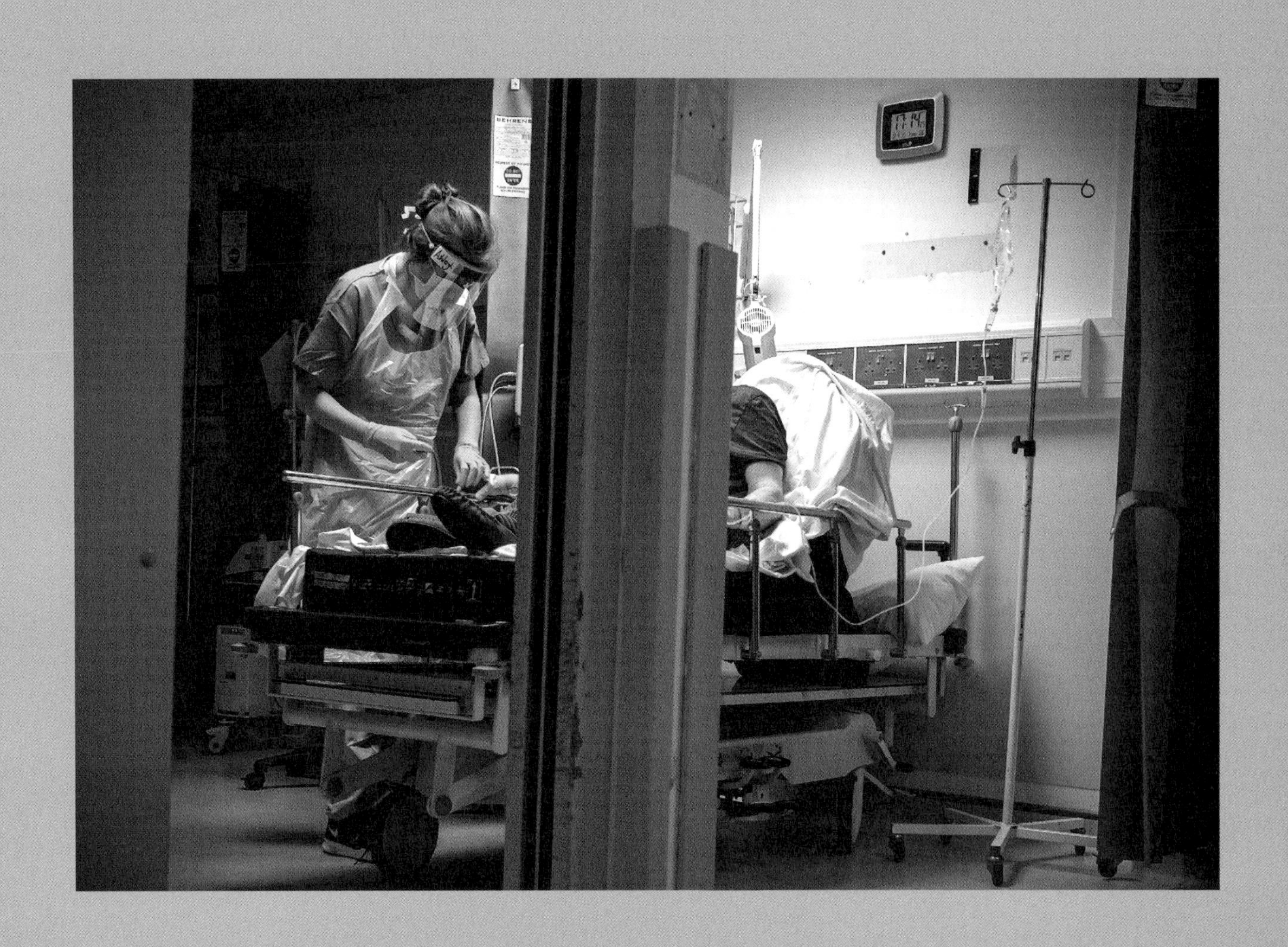

144
184/84
05:04
05:04
02:04
DELL

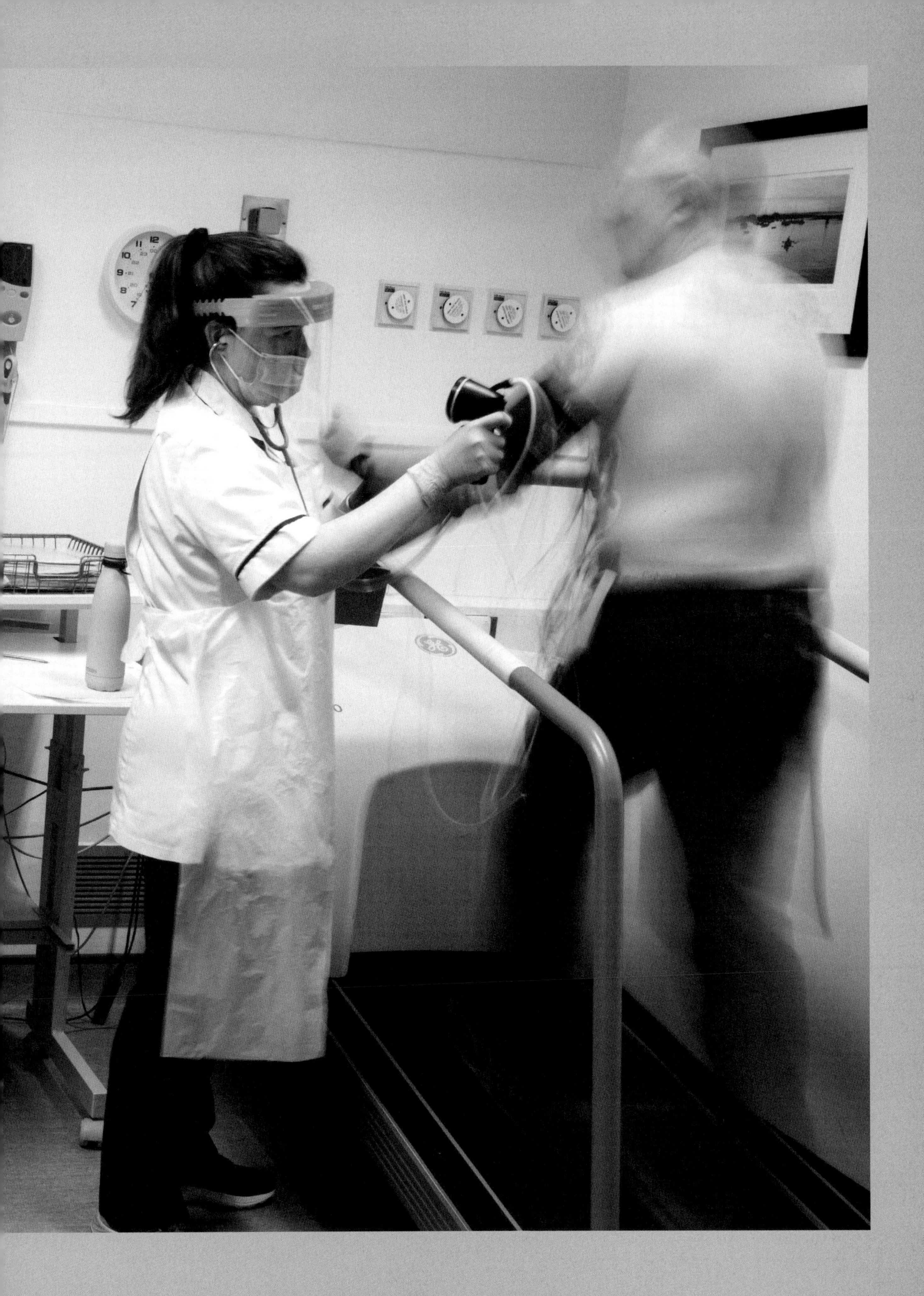

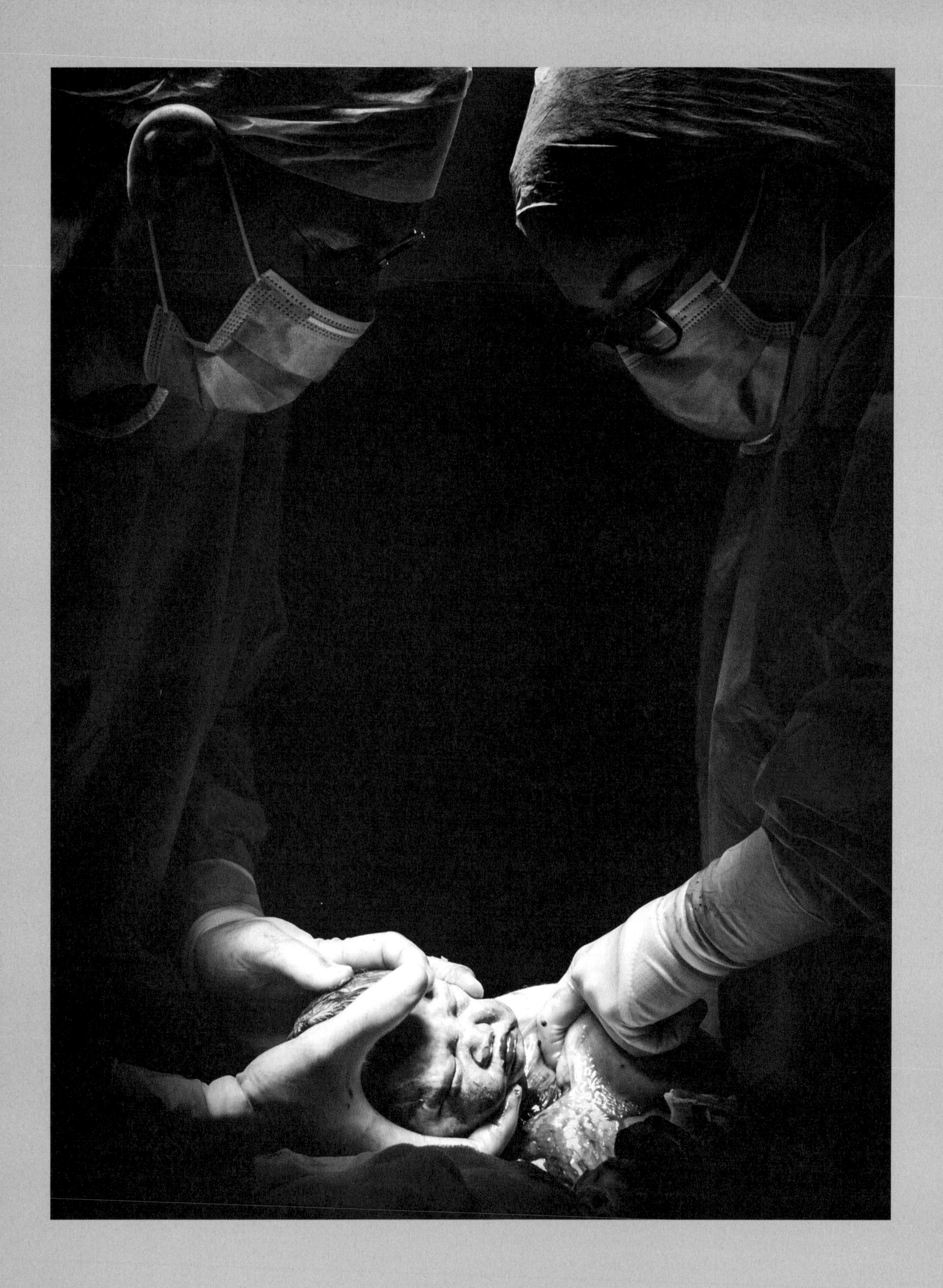

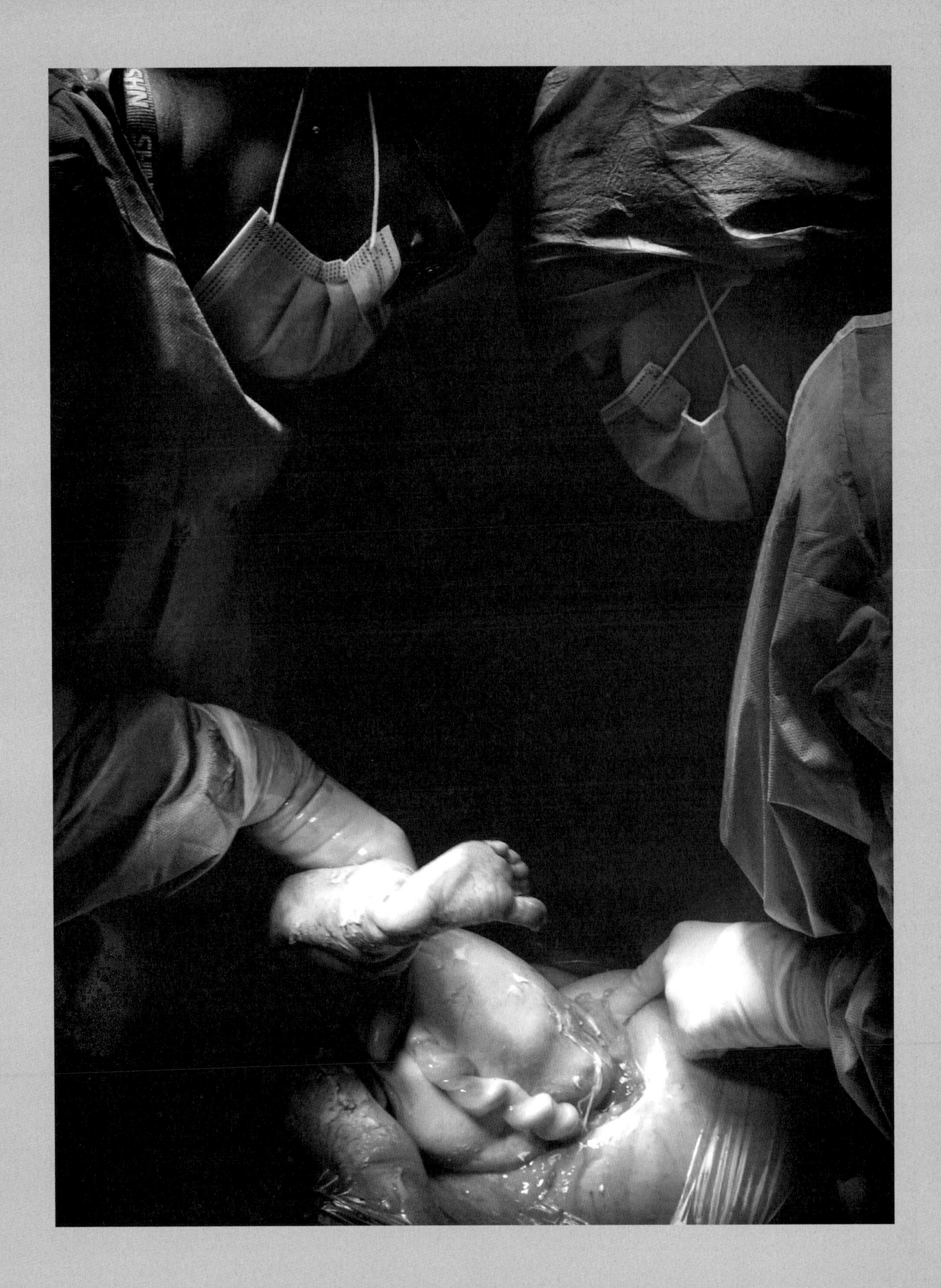
NHS

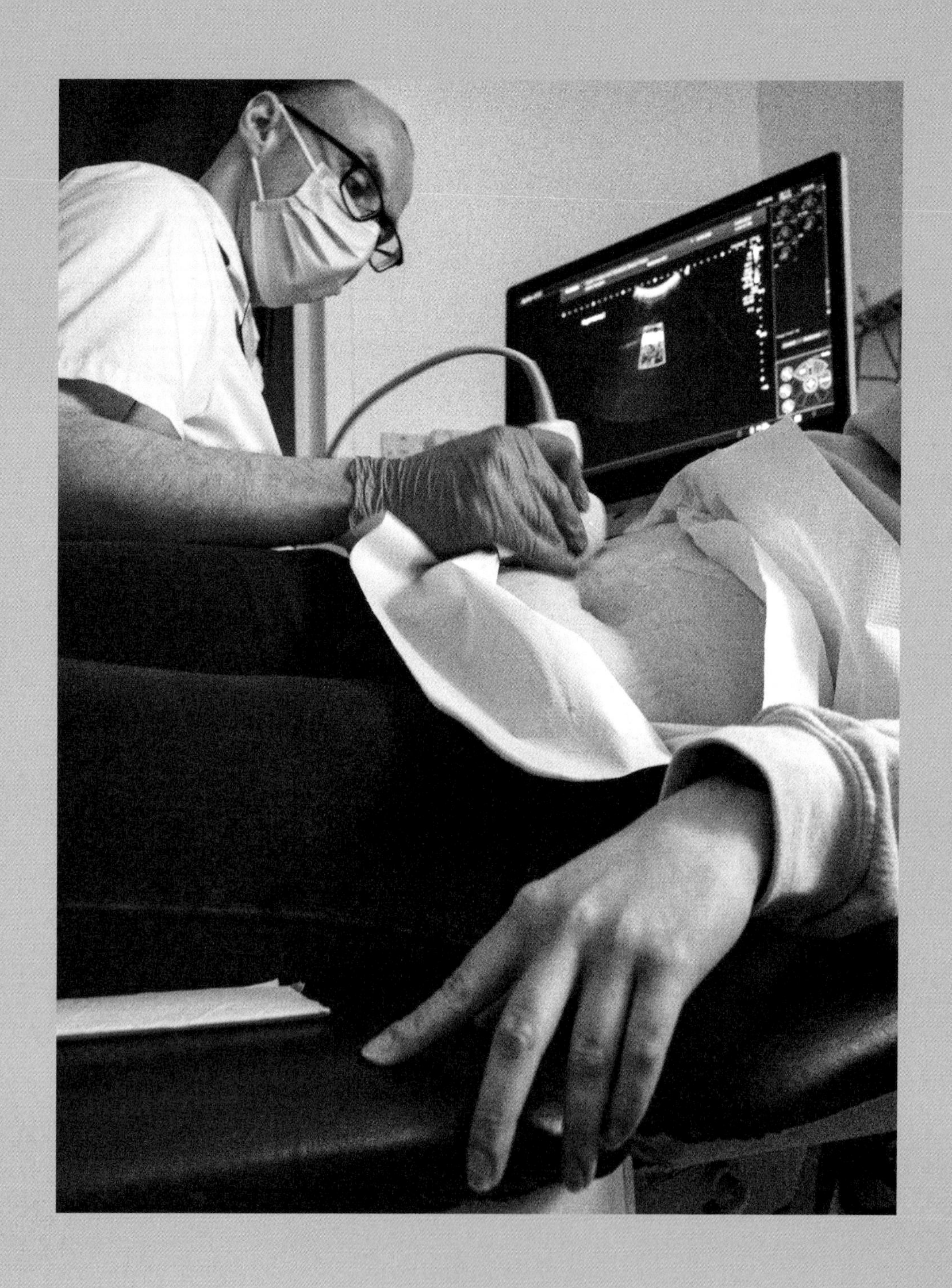

## RADIOLOGY

COVID-19 represented a tidal wave of anxiety and uncertainty which would change imaging operations significantly. An enormous collective team effort from SEHSCT Radiology ensured appropriate and timely responses to the waves of the pandemic and lasting benefits to our patients and staff.

Open and honest leadership and daily communication encouraged a newly found staff resilience and togetherness in the early waves of the response. All staff groups, old and new, worked together to manage the surge in chest imaging, notably portable imaging on the wards and Emergency Department. Our CT team responded resolutely with a dedicated COVID service.

With significant resources dedicated to the COVID response, Radiology outpatient operations were rapidly suspended, creating numerous challenges with short and long term implications. A renewed focus on Red Flag and Urgent imaging within MRI and Ultrasound ensured we could expedite clinical pathways, including rapid discharge to support hospital services colleagues.

The COVID-19 response created a momentum for change in Radiology. Staff collectively responded to every challenge presented by this unprecedented disease; however, it was not without consequence. Exhaustion, frustration, and anxiety were consistently reported as staff groups began to recognise the importance of an appropriate work/life balance.

Images of heavily PPE cladded colleagues are a great source of pride and reflection. We also fondly remember several Radiology colleagues who passed away during the dark days of the past two years.

Michael Ennis
Trust MRI Lead

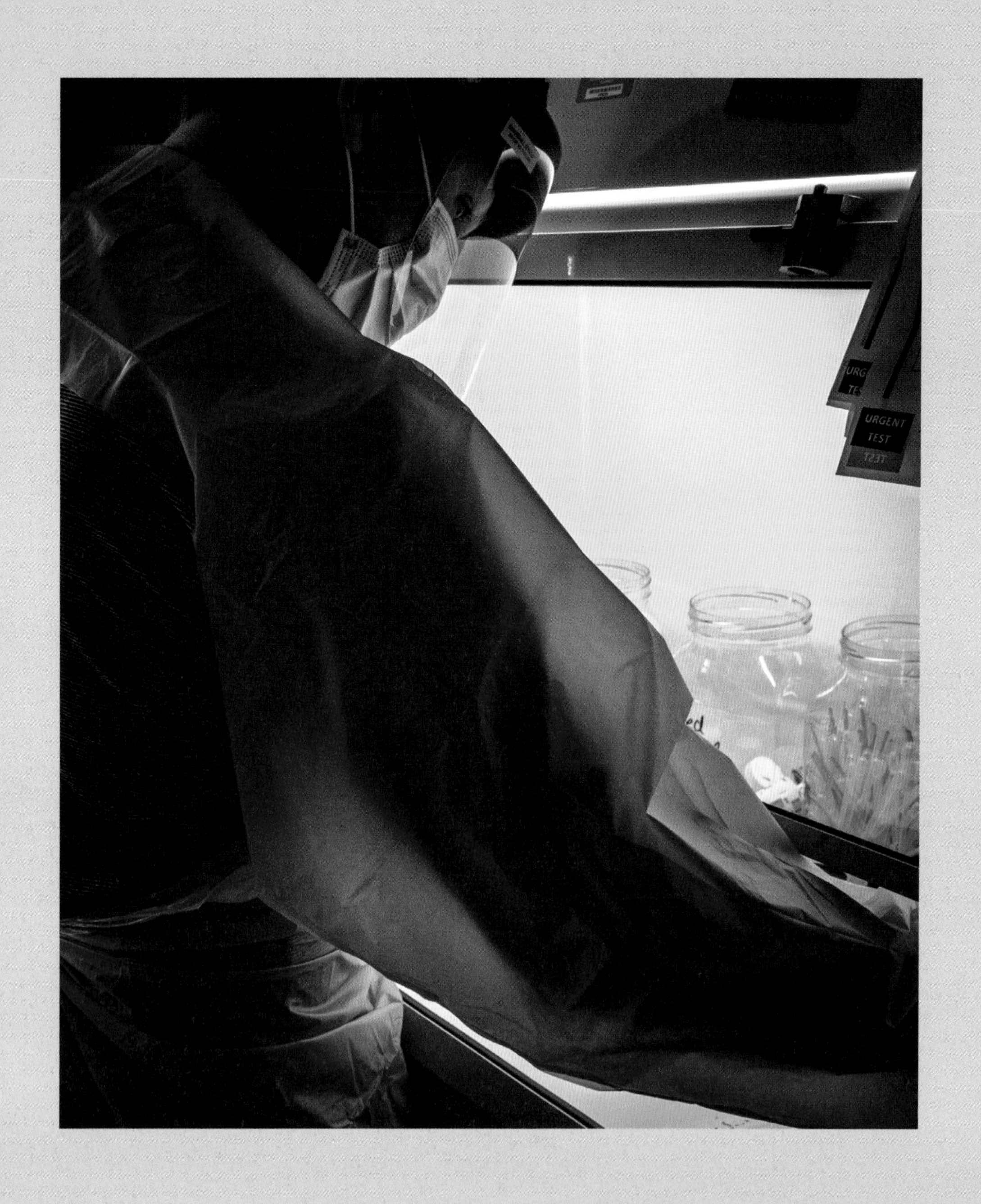
URGENT
TEST

## LABORATORIES

Like many hospital services, life changed for the laboratories when the pandemic hit. Routine workload fell quite dramatically as both primary and secondary care focused their attention on the pandemic response and temporarily stood down many routine services.

The impact on laboratories was that while routine testing declined, the demand for COVID-19 testing rose exponentially. This led to a worldwide demand for test kits and equipment and resulted in laboratory staff being re-deployed to meet this new demand. Initially the COVID-19 testing was outsourced but in May 2020 the SEHSCT began its own testing. Staff had to quickly learn new skills, find new ways of working and in some cases work outside their normal specialist areas. It was also necessary to support the service using agency staff.

The laboratories also had to carry out risk assessments and introduce safeguarding measures to help keep staff safe. Some staff had to shield and several face-to-face interactions ceased with meetings now taking place virtually.

As routine testing gradually returns and as HSC services rebuild across Northern Ireland, the continuing challenge for laboratories will be to manage pre-pandemic levels of routine alongside any demands for ongoing COVID-19 testing and to implement any lessons learnt along the way.

Raymond Gamble
Laboratory Service Manager

Are you a Student Nurse / Midwife
in Year 2 or above?
South Eastern HSC Trust?
Join our Bank as a
Band 3 Senior Nursing Assistant
Email:
for an application form

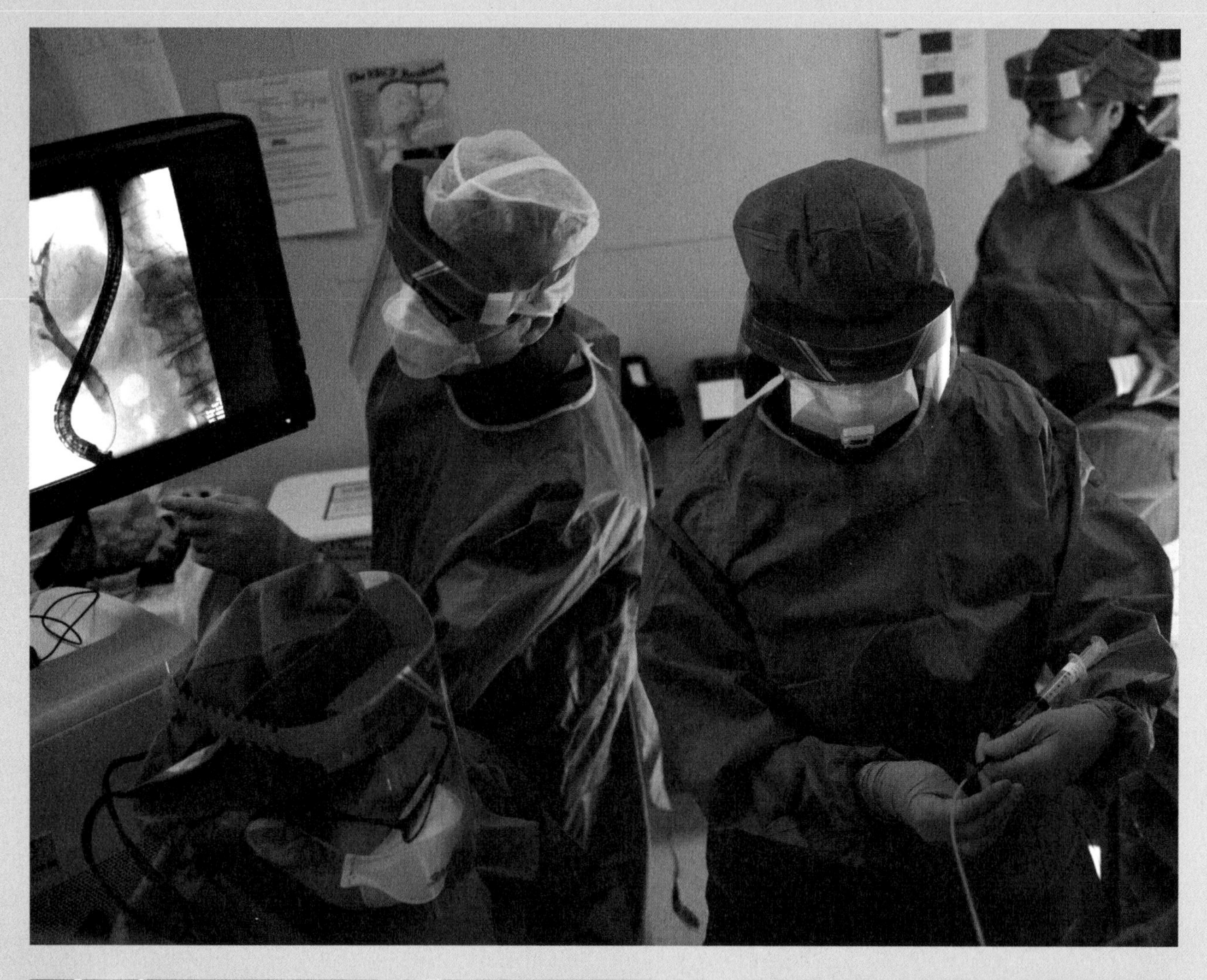

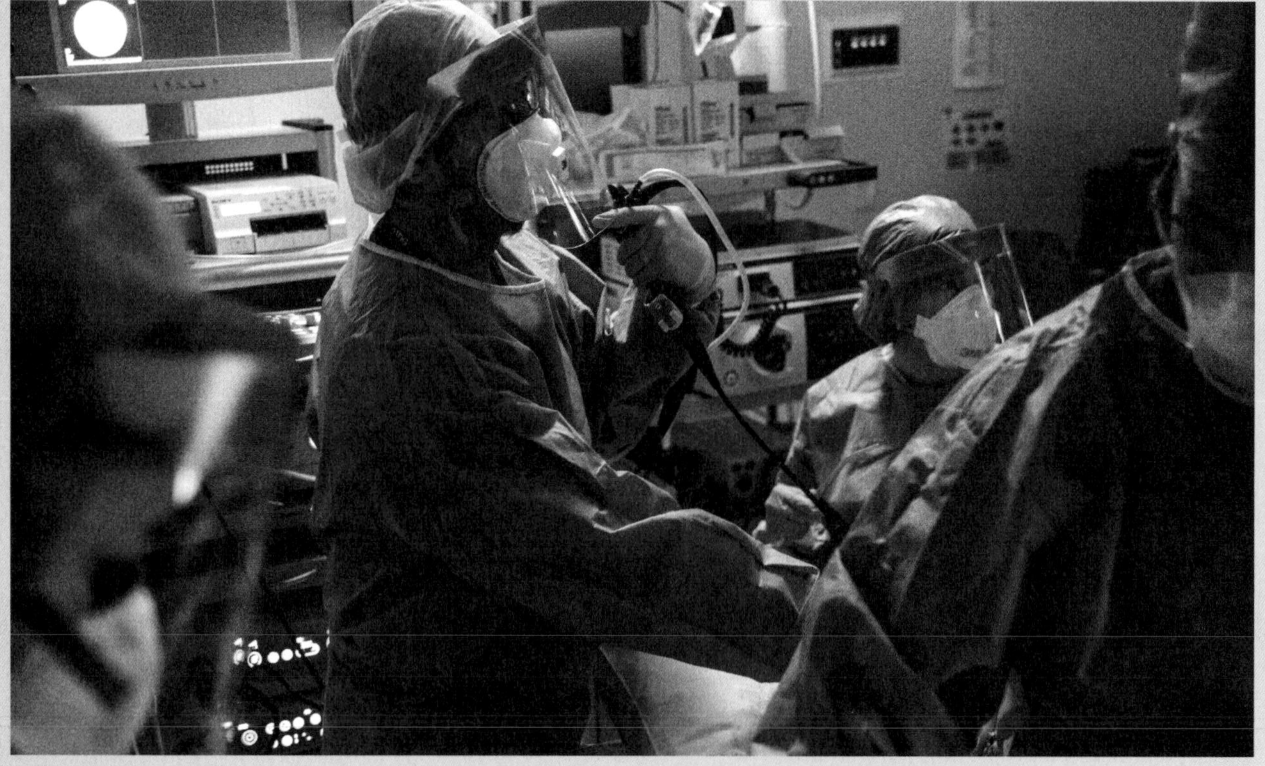

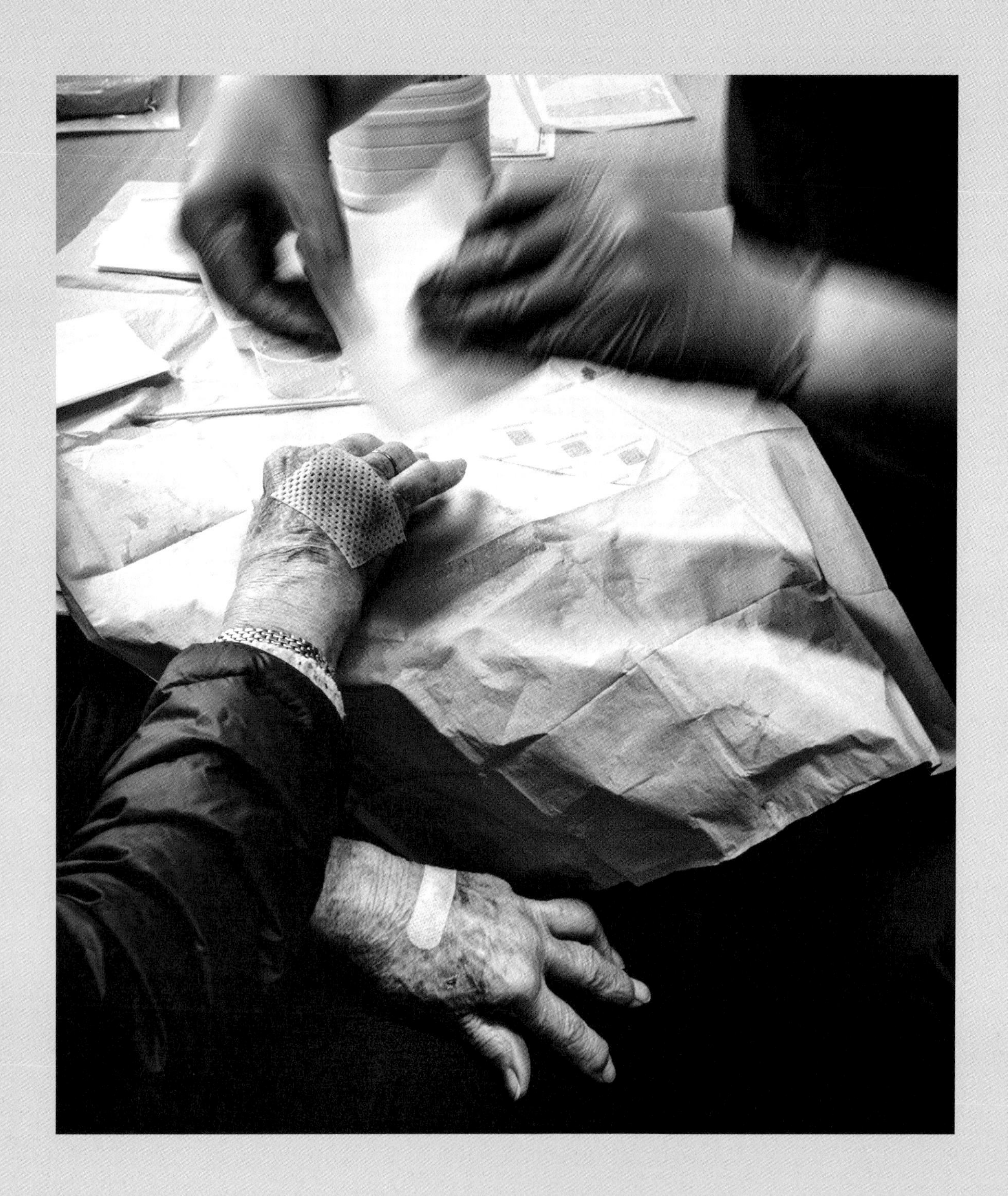

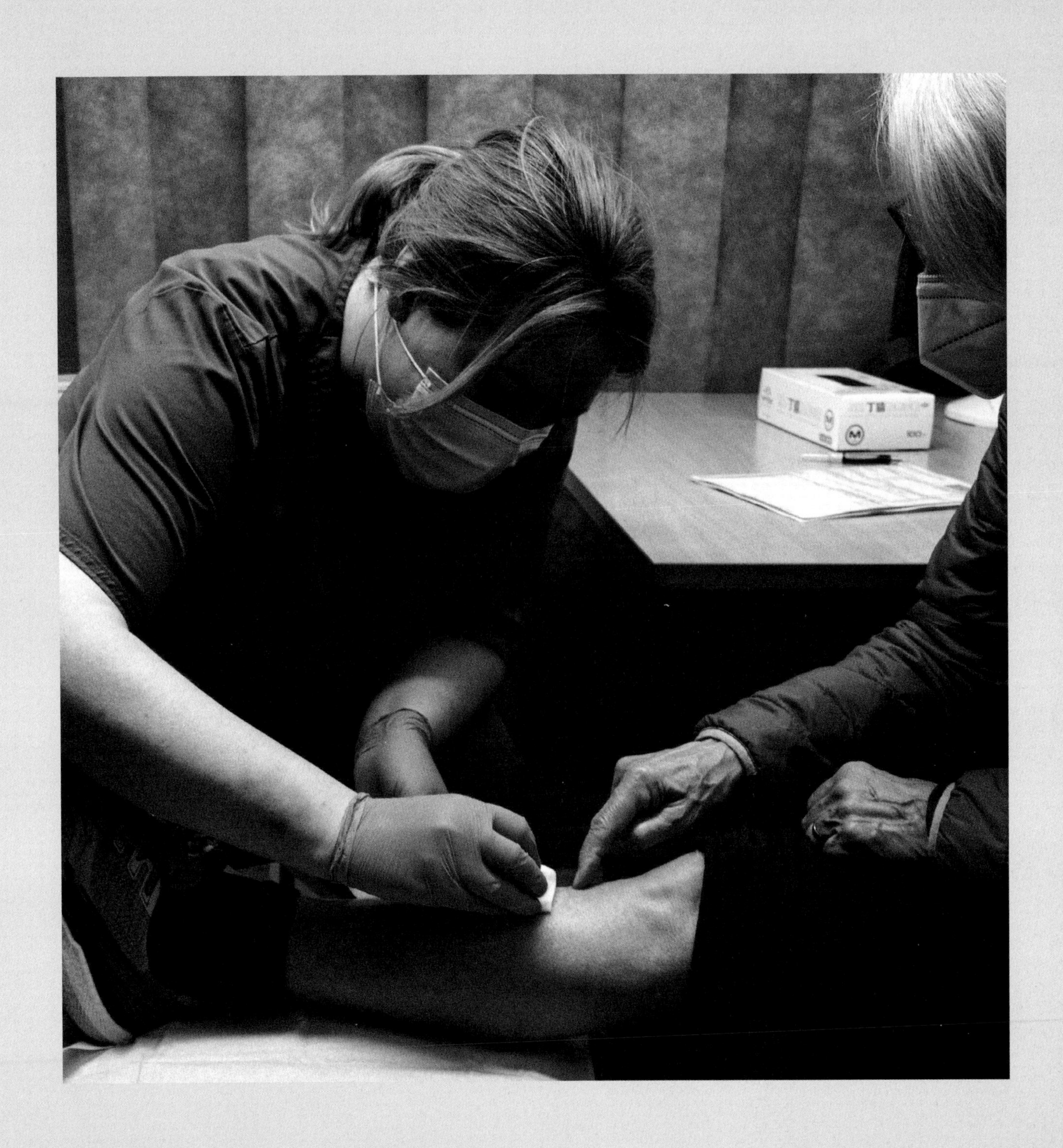

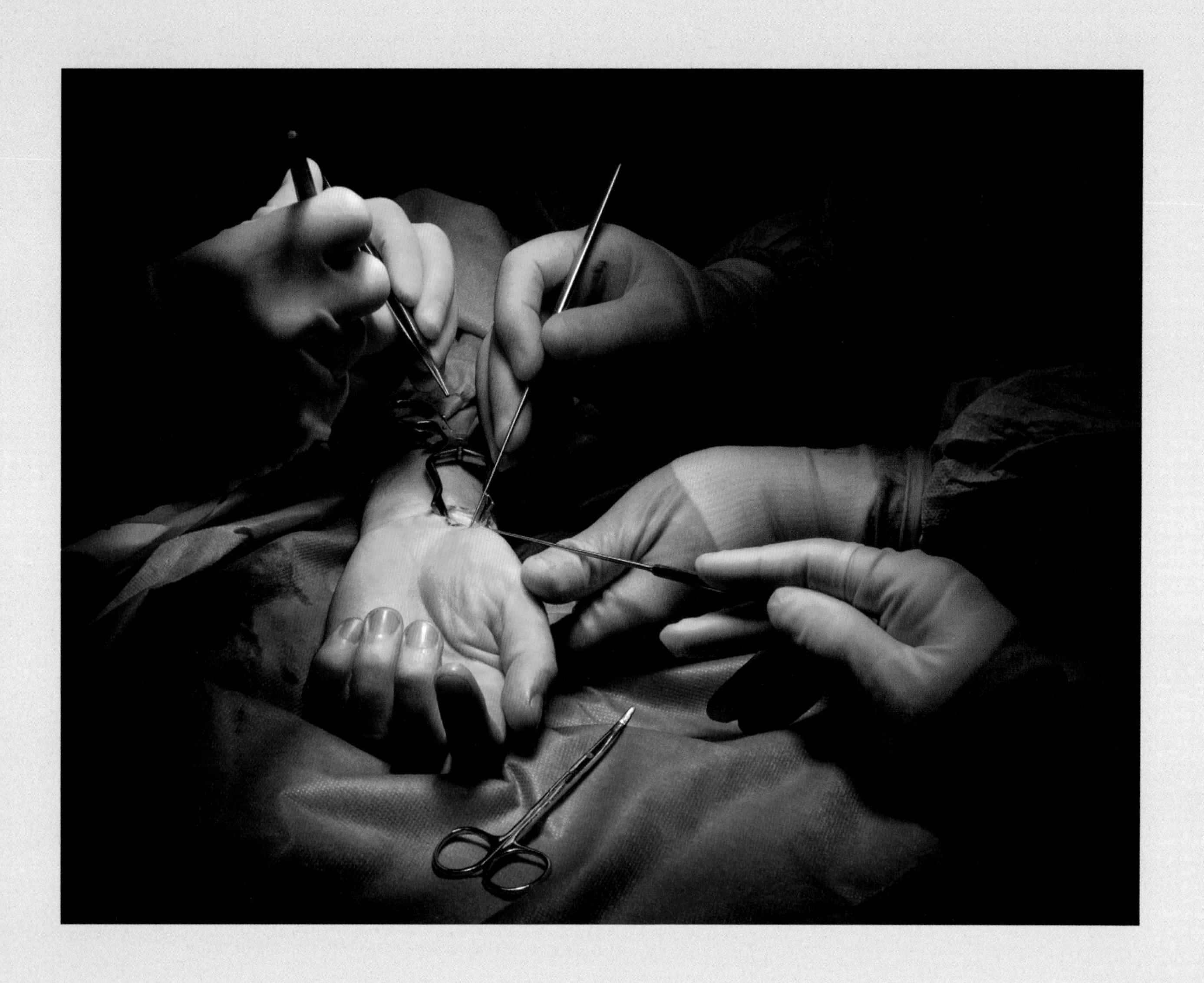

## THEATRES & RECOVERY

By March 2020 COVID-19 contingency plans were rapidly being developed across the SEHSCT. In theatres and recovery, a huge effort to identify and reorganise every possible resource began in preparation for the ominous health emergency ahead.

Staff from the Lagan Valley Hospital and the Downe Hospital joined the team at the Ulster Hospital where roles were redefined & new skill sets quickly developed to support the ICU.

Main recovery ward was set up to serve as an additional intensive care facility so main theatre staff relocated to the Day Procedure Unit (DPU) where both teams amalgamated quickly initially to continue cover for emergency, trauma and urgent cancer surgeries.

This reconfiguration of services provided a green pathway for surgical patients and represented a huge effort of will and determination. Very quickly the service expanded so that all four DPU theatres were running at full capacity.

After the first peak, recovery ward were able to step down ICU provision and main theatre work gradually resumed. Theatre staff from DPU moved back to main theatre to allow the rebuilding of theatre services. As many staff were still working in ICU the two services remained combined, but Lagan Valley Hospital and Downe Hospital were able to resume day surgery at their normal locations.

It took two years for all staff to return to their normal jobs and we are now planning the return to full capacity with ambitious plans to expand further.

The past two years have demonstrated that the strength and wealth of an organisation lies in the expertise and quality of its teams. We recognise the true value of a collaborative culture and are so proud of our department.

Kim Irwin
Anaesthetic Assistant

Elaine Vogan
Theatre Sister

an act,
TO B

NO VIDEO
NO VIDEO
NO VIDEO
DANGER MOVING BARRIER
NO VIDEO

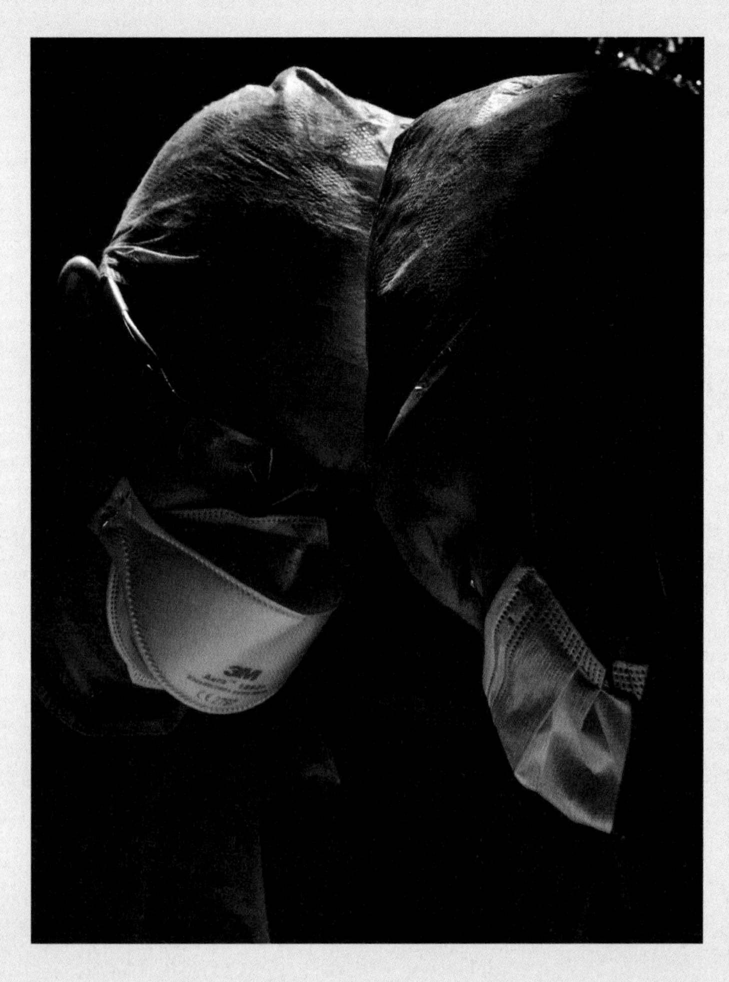
3M

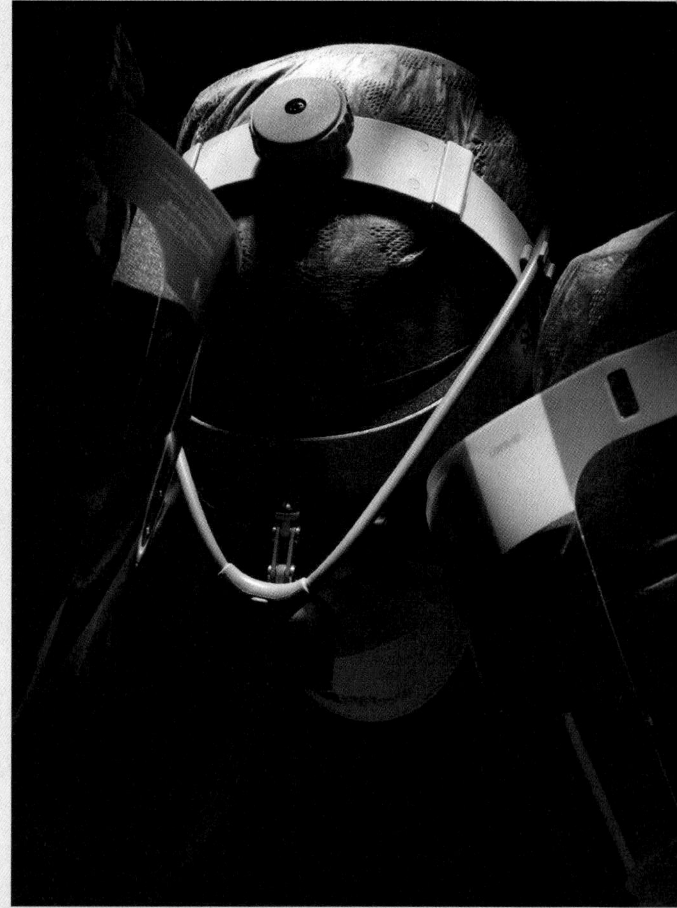

RECEPTION

## VACCINATION

Eight months into the COVID-19 pandemic there was finally some good news when the first COVID-19 vaccine was approved in November 2020.

Trusts were tasked with the delivery of vaccines as quickly and safely as possible to the most vulnerable and those who cared for them. The Trust Project Team set to work and within four weeks a mobile vaccination team and a vaccination centre were set up. Staff visited 111 Care Homes over a 10-day period to deliver vaccines to residents and staff while frontline staff were vaccinated in the Ulster Hospital Vaccination Centre.

Many staff across all disciplines worked additional hours and some retired colleagues returned to practice supporting the vaccination programme 12 hours per day, seven days per week. The service grew rapidly, opening to members of the public with upwards of 1,200 vaccines delivered daily.

A total of 128,485 COVID-19 vaccines were administered in the Ulster Hospital before the service transferred to the Regional Mass Vaccination Centre in the SSE Arena, Belfast which was hosted by the SEHSC Trust.

In total 618,000 doses of COVID-19 vaccine were administered by the Trust in just 15 months.

Tanya Daly
Clinical Lead
COVID-19 Vaccination Programme

Meeting
Platform
cisco

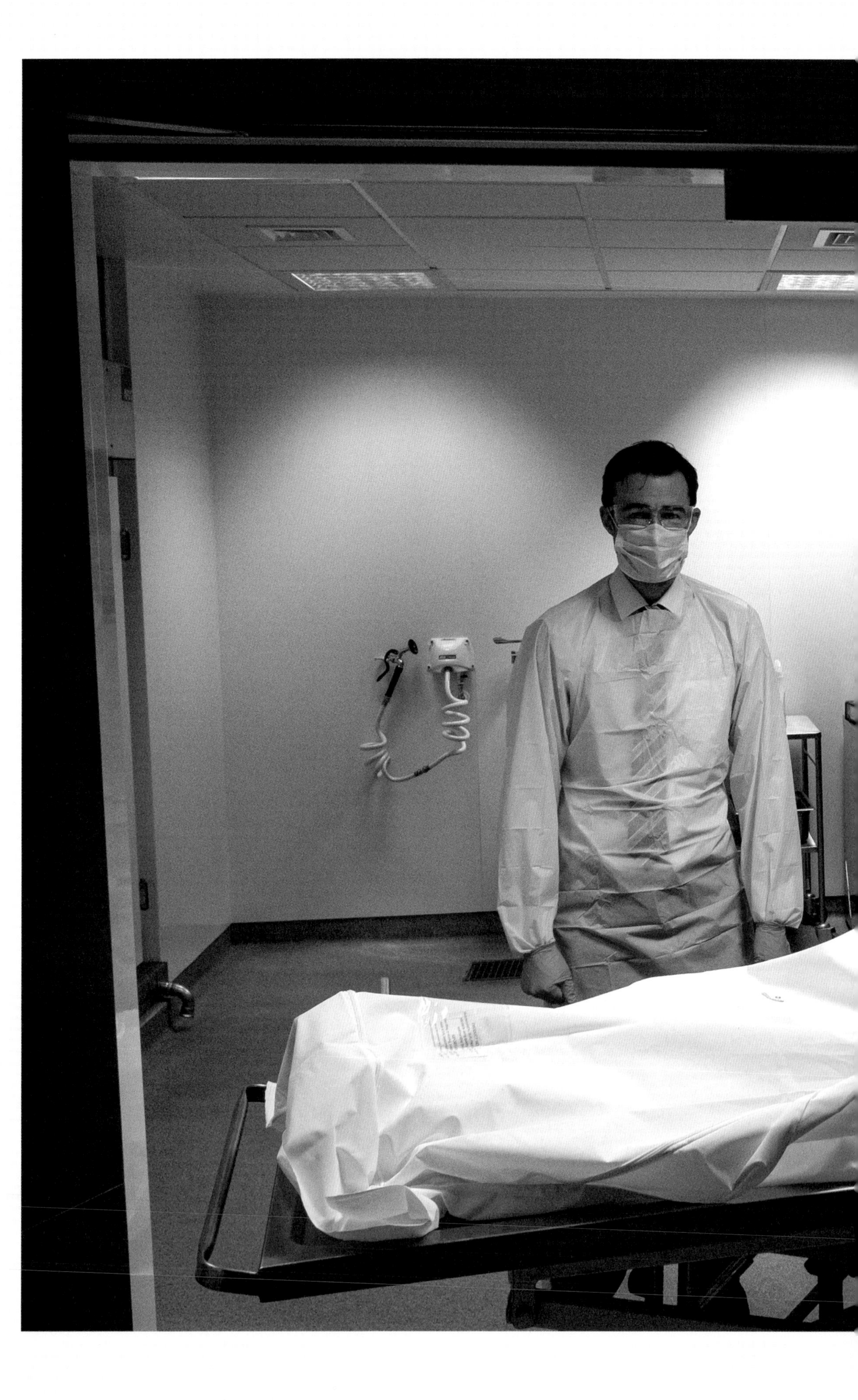

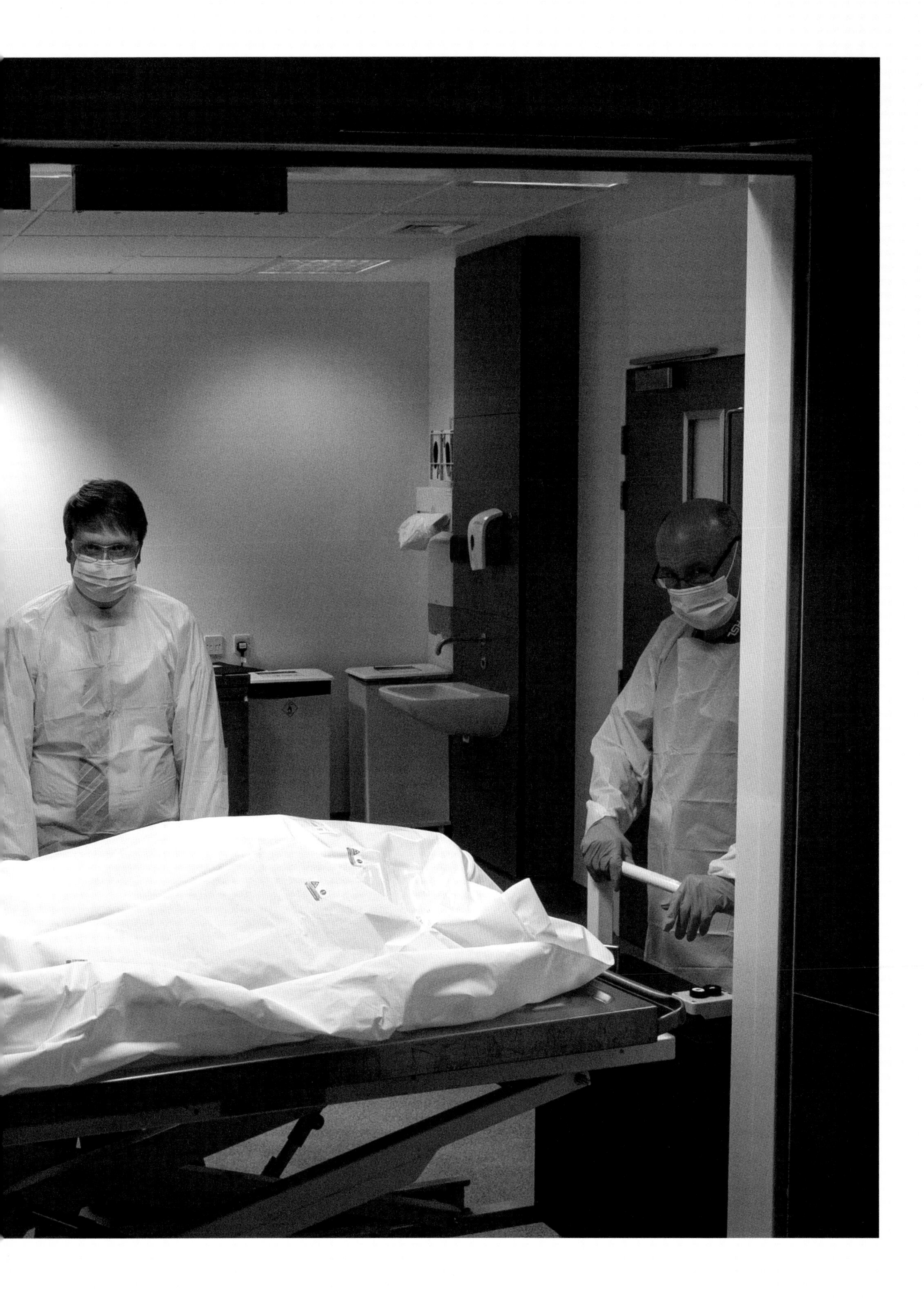

FIRE BLANKET

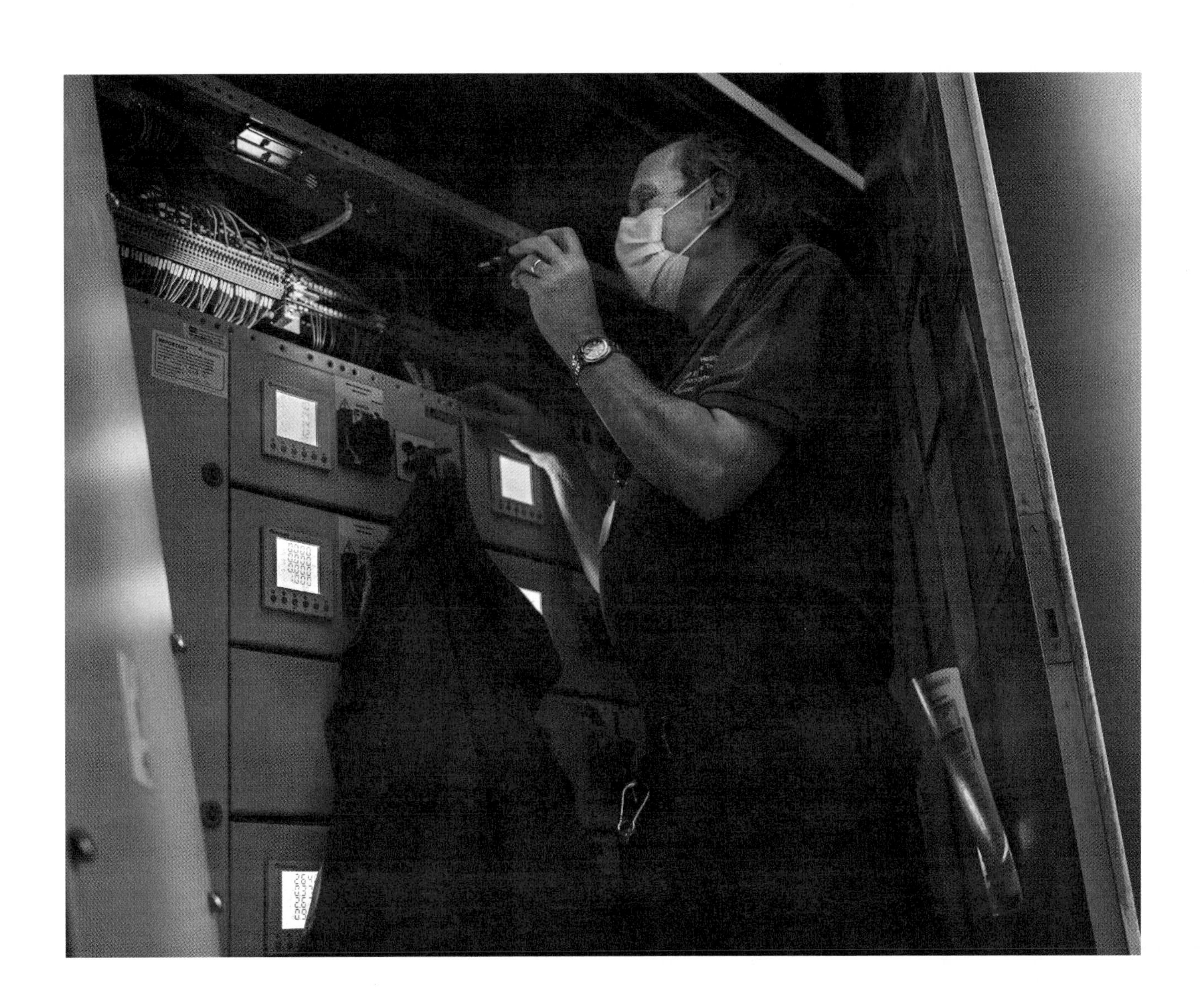

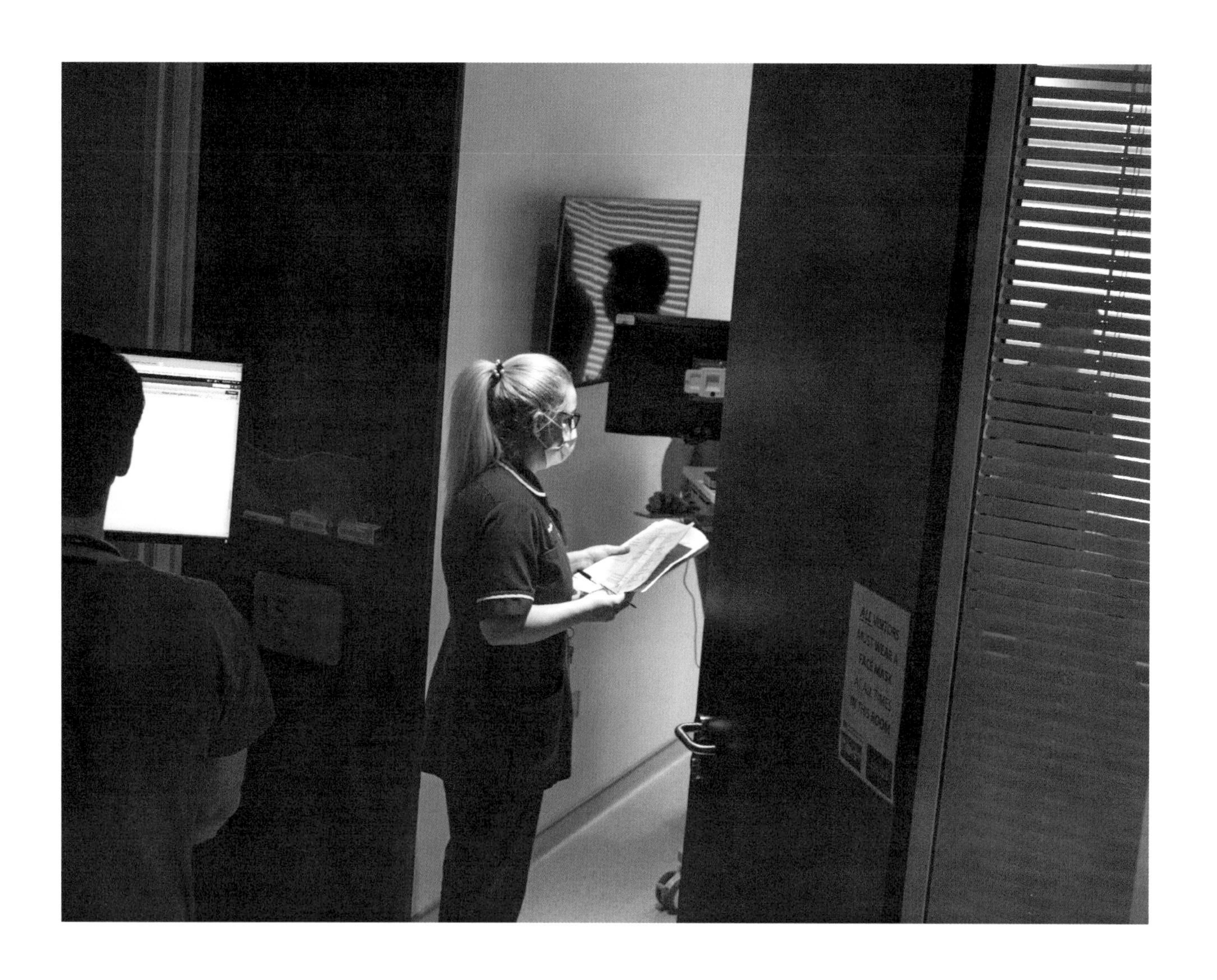
ALL VISITORS
MUST WEAR A
FACE MASK
AT ALL TIMES
IN THIS ROOM

## MEDICAL WARDS

From the beginning of the pandemic, we had staff redeployed from community and specialist nurse posts. This was very difficult for them as some had not worked in a ward setting for many years. Having to wear PPE and not being able to see facial expressions was difficult for both staff and patients as identification can be an issue. The heat, headaches and dehydration from wearing the PPE added to the stress level. The reconfiguration of tearooms and limitation of numbers during staff breaks due to social distancing added to staff's frustration.

Visitation of relatives was stopped during the first lock down and this generated high levels of anxiety among families. Hence nursing and medical staff contacted families and provided daily updates. As we moved through the pandemic, visitation was re-established but under tight constraints and limitations. Records of visitors had to be kept daily and slots had to be booked to avoid overcrowding. Virtual visitation was also set up. Although these were time-consuming processes for the nursing staff, it was gratifying to enable family-patient interactions.

We had outbreaks of COVID-19 in some of the wards. Patients in bays who were contacts had to be isolated and it was sometimes challenging to find enough single rooms.

Almost all the medical ward staff have had COVID-19 infection to varying degrees. Some had been hospitalised and many still have lingering complications.

The pandemic has given us all cause for reflection. It has changed many of our working practices, re-emphasised the importance of communication and showed the important role visitors play in patients' recovery. We are a stronger team and more prepared now to face new challenges.

Audrey Christie
Ward Sister

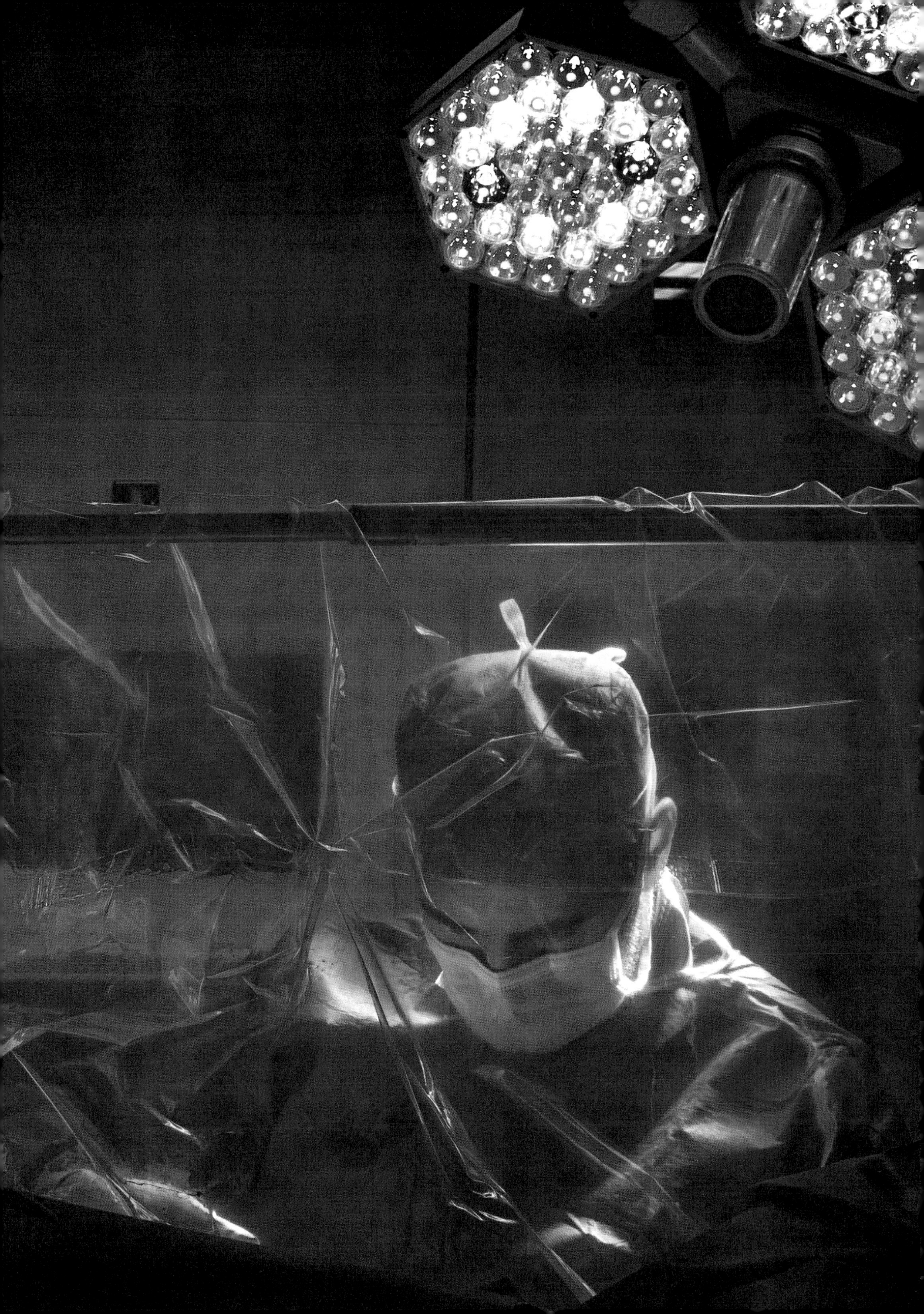

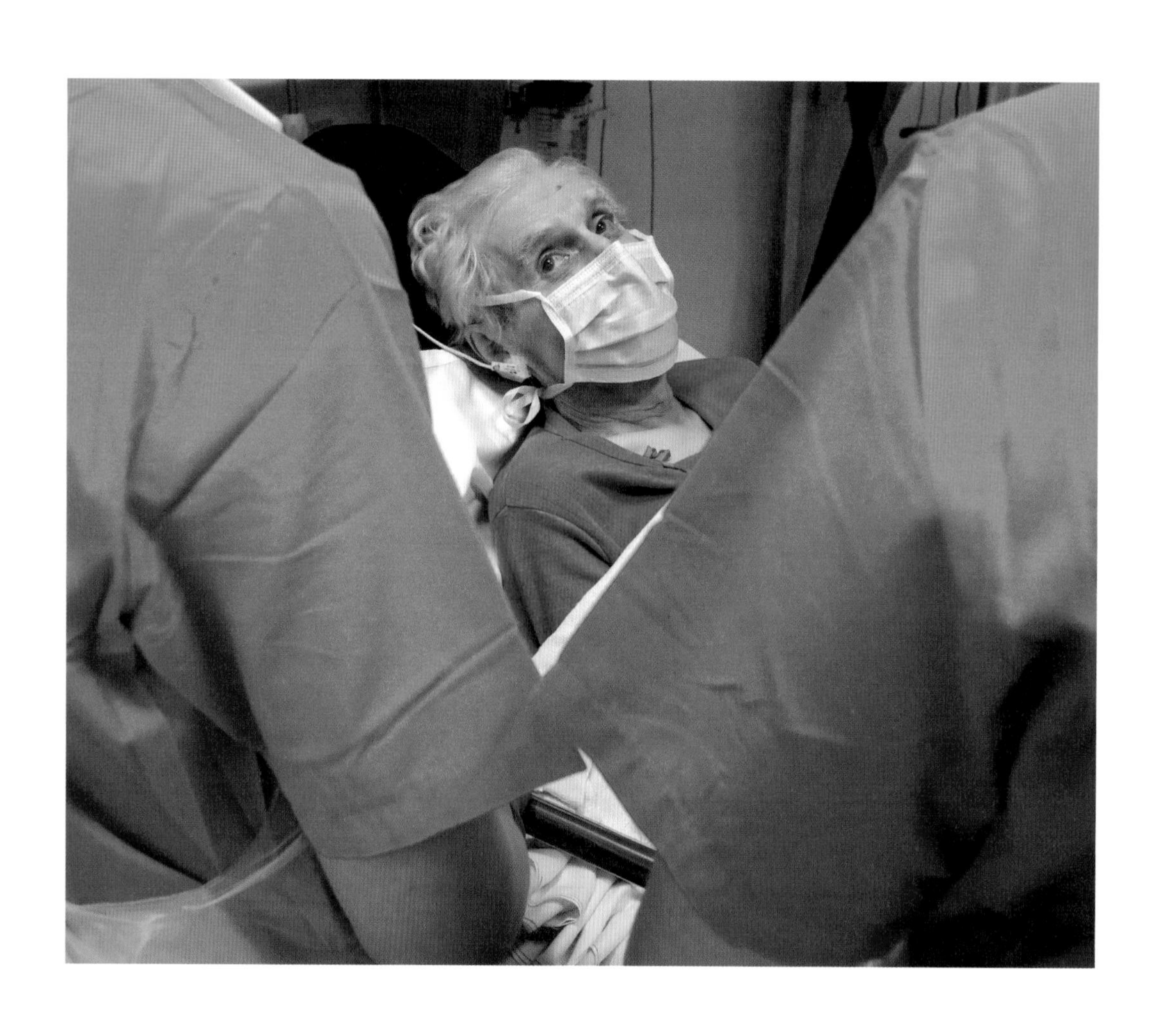

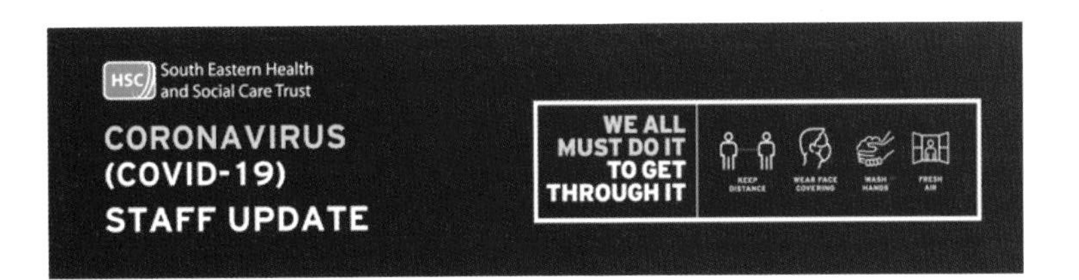


**19 August 2021**

## Fit Testing Website

The new Fit Testing Site is now live on iConnect, click here to access the site.

Managers and staff can find information in relation to:

- New starts requiring FFP3s
- Retesting
- How to prepare for a Fit Test
- FFP3 Mask Fitting Guides
- How to perform a Fit Check
- Alternative Arrangements for Staff who fail a Fit Test

To arrange an appointment for Fit Testing contact Fit Test Scheduling on (028) 92 680 802, internal extension 71154 or email fit.testing@setrust.hscni.net

## Face Coverings

Advice on the use of Face Masks and Face Coverings in all health and social care settings has been issued by the Department of Health.

This guidance is applicable to healthcare workers as well as visitors and patients entering Trust facilities. Please take the opportunity to read this advice click here so that we continue to implement good practice and reduce the spread of COVID-19.

**In July the Trust commenced the process of sourcing face coverings for all of our staff and we have managed to purchase masks which should arrive at the end of August or beginning of September, 2020. All our staff will be issued with two face coverings each.**

We would recommend that, as well as complying with the advice on face coverings, our staff continue to apply the following principles;

- Continue to social distance always apply the 2 metre rule. When this cannot be applied wear a face mask or face covering. Whatever is chosen will be dependent on the role and the working environment of the member of staff
- Wash hands often
- Stay off work if you develop COVID-19 symptoms
- Exercise respiratory etiquette. Catch coughs and sneezes into a tissue "catch it, bin it, kill it," or cover your mouth when covering and sneezing with your arm

## Social Distancing Reminder

As patients and visitors and staff who have been shielding begin to return to our hospitals it is vital that we continue to practice social distancing. We should stop to consider our current work practices and establish if there are different ways to practice social distancing for example:

- Do not sit beside each other in large groups especially at times of relaxation
- Only have the number of chairs in your staff room to allow social distancing
- Consider 2M markings in your workplace, except where surface cleaning would be compromised
- Don't be afraid to remind colleagues (nicely) that you need your 2M space
- Social distancing also applies to lifts so if the lift is small, wait for the next one.

**Please remember if you have COVID-19 symptoms, you MUST stay at home and self-isolate. If you do not have symptoms, social distancing is extremely important for you.**

WARNING
HOT SURFACE

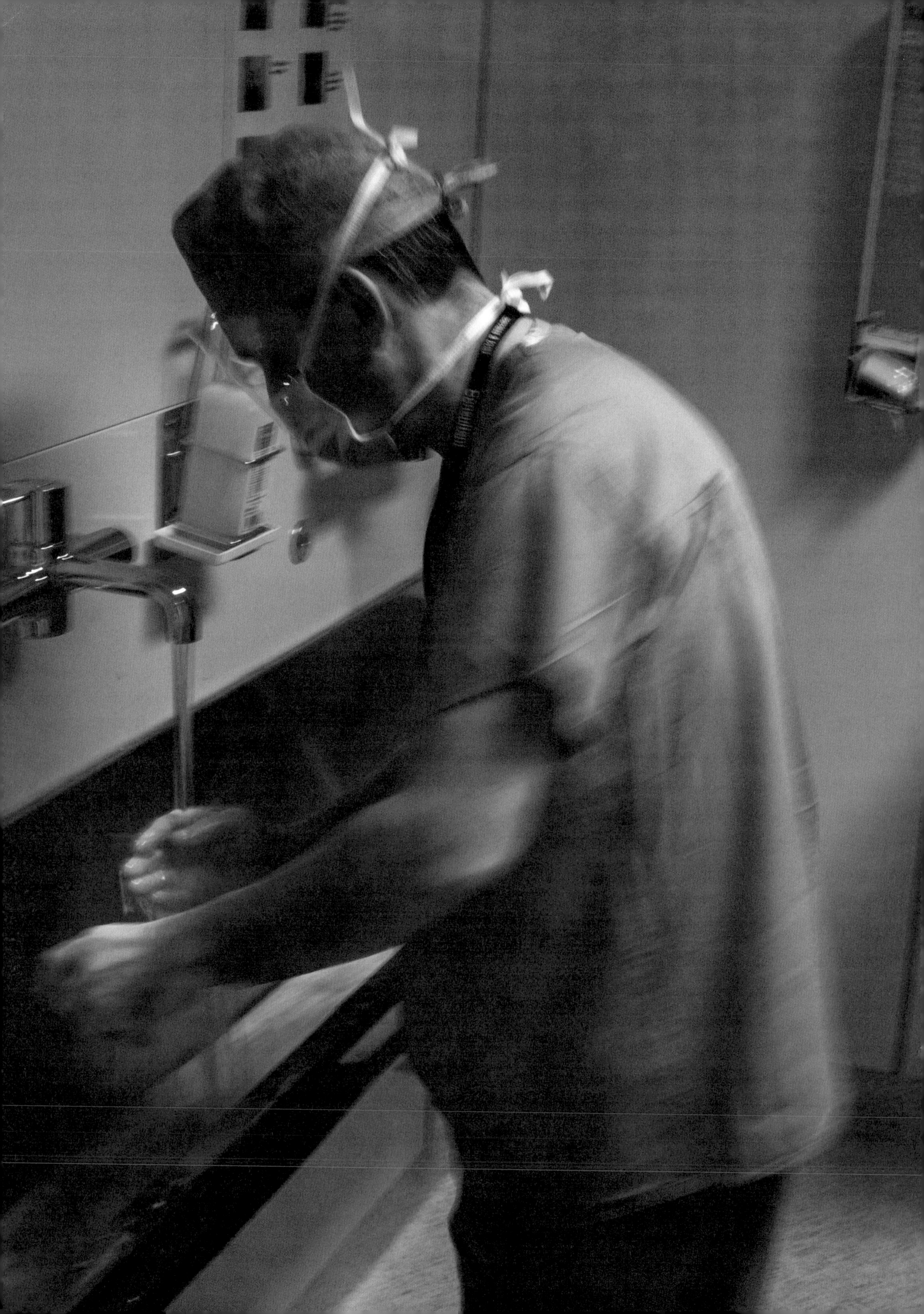

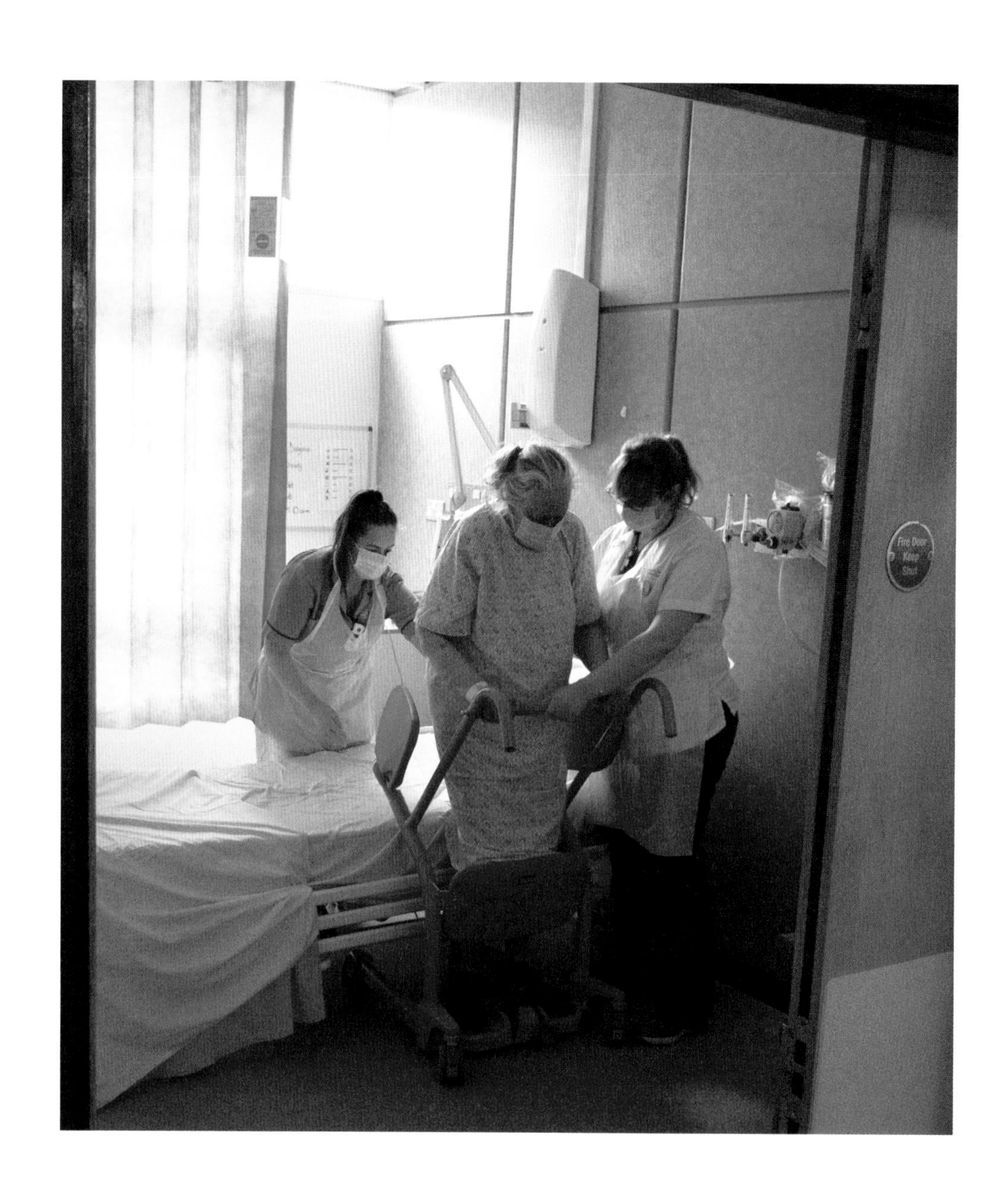
Fire Door
Keep
Shut

## PHYSIOTHERAPY

The physiotherapy service had to adapt and change its working pattern right from the beginning of the pandemic. Because of delivery of service in many high-risk environments (for example ICU, ED, wards and patients' homes) across the Trust, this created a significant amount of stress and anxiety among the staff and their family members.

There was redeployment of staff from outside the hospital to work in acute ward settings. Additional training and reskilling were required especially in the care of respiratory patients. There was also an impact from staff who needed to be shielded from direct face-to-face patient care. New and appropriate roles were sought for them so as to maximise the use of their skills. We also had to provide respiratory training for redeployed non-acute nursing and medical staff.

Initially because of the lockdown, appointments for sporting related injuries decreased. This allowed staff to be able to look after the increased number of respiratory patients and to prioritise and to facilitate discharges from hospitals thus maximising the number of available beds in the Trust. Staff hours changed to shift pattern working to provide access to physiotherapy care for longer periods throughout the week.

Good communication has always been a vital part of physiotherapy assessment and treatment. With social distancing and the use of PPE, direct face-to-face communication with patients created a large challenge. Like many other departments, we increased use of telephone and virtual assessments to allow less disruption to outpatient service.

Richard Porter
Emergency Department Physiotherapist

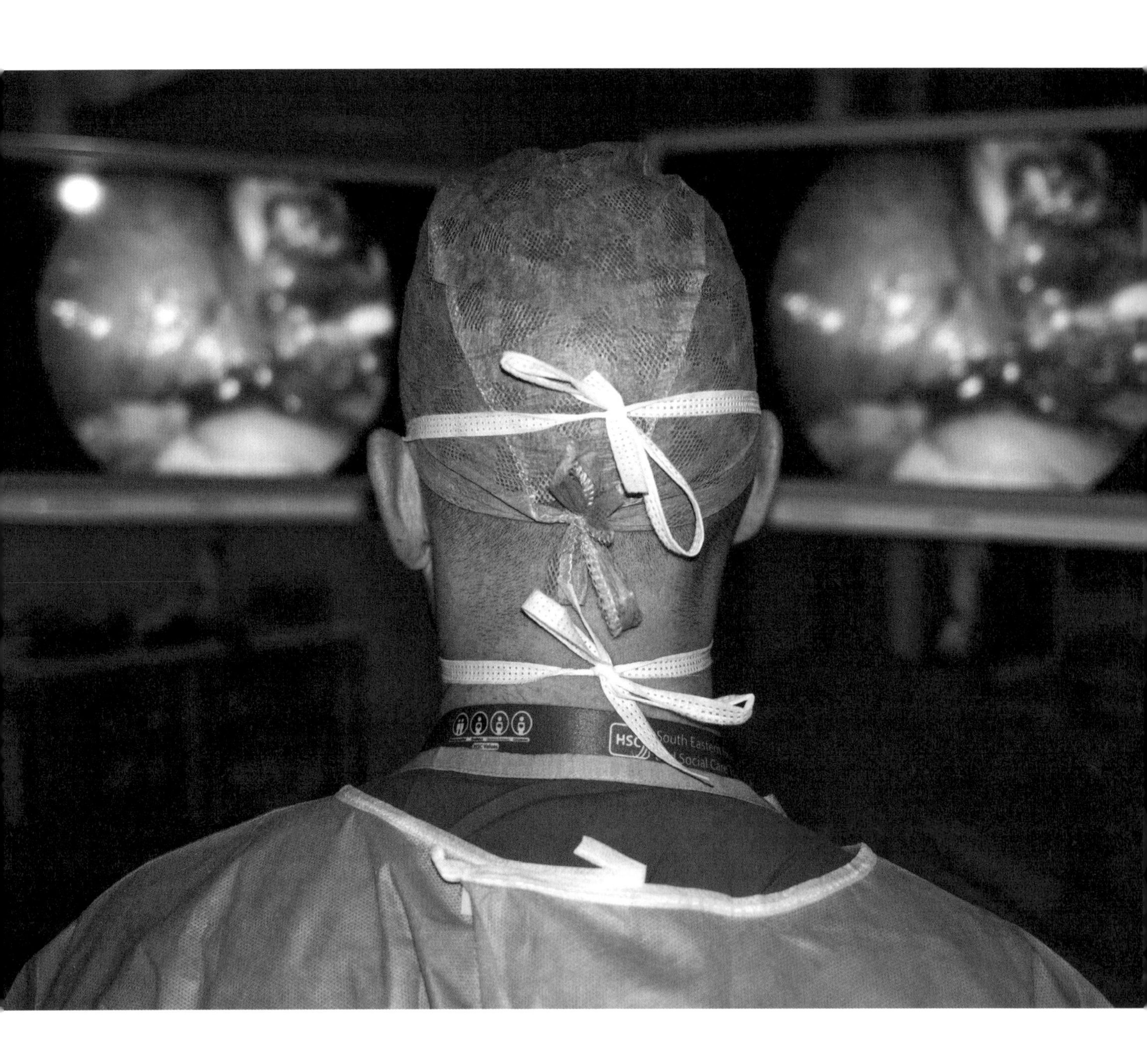
HSC
South
Social

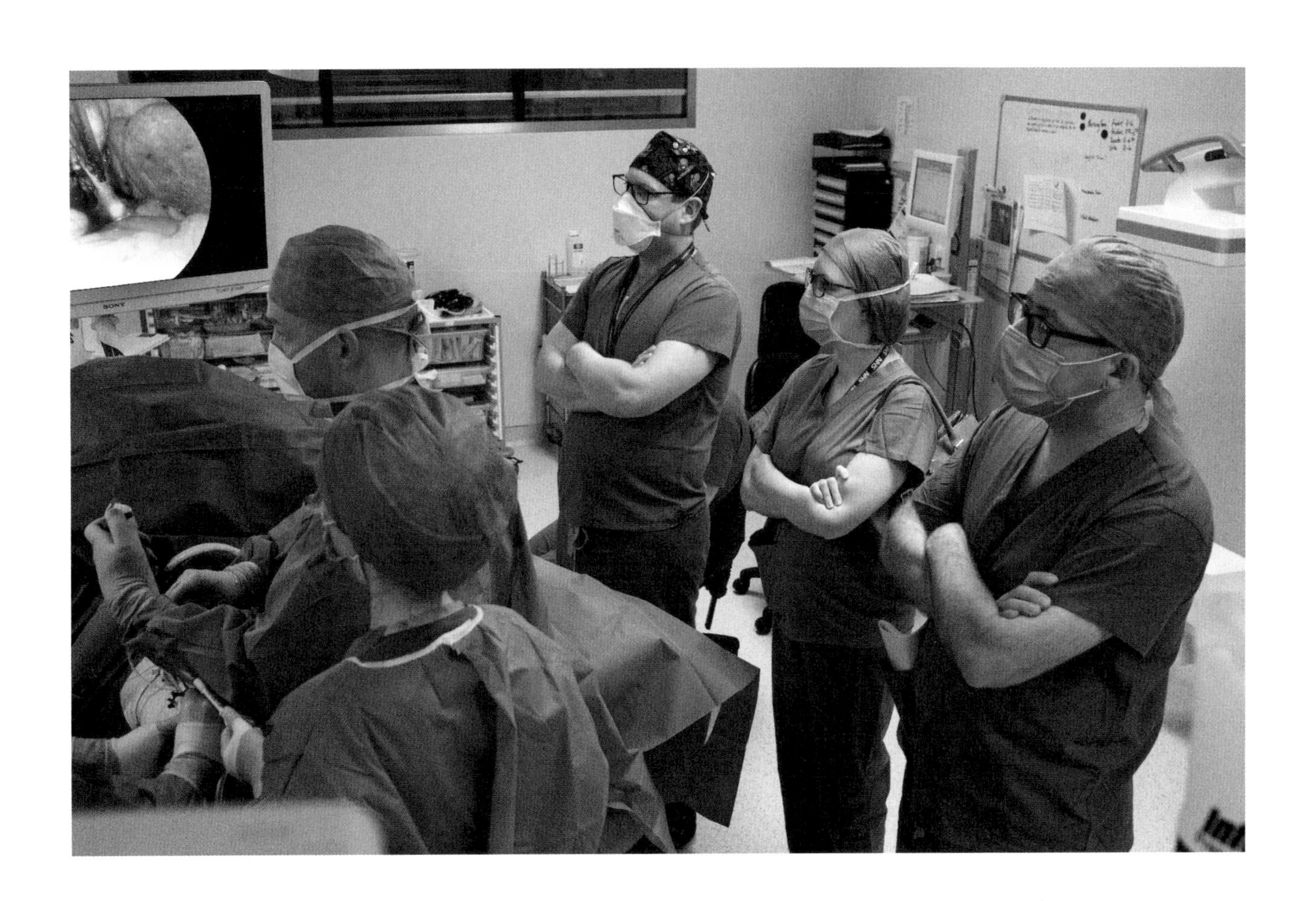

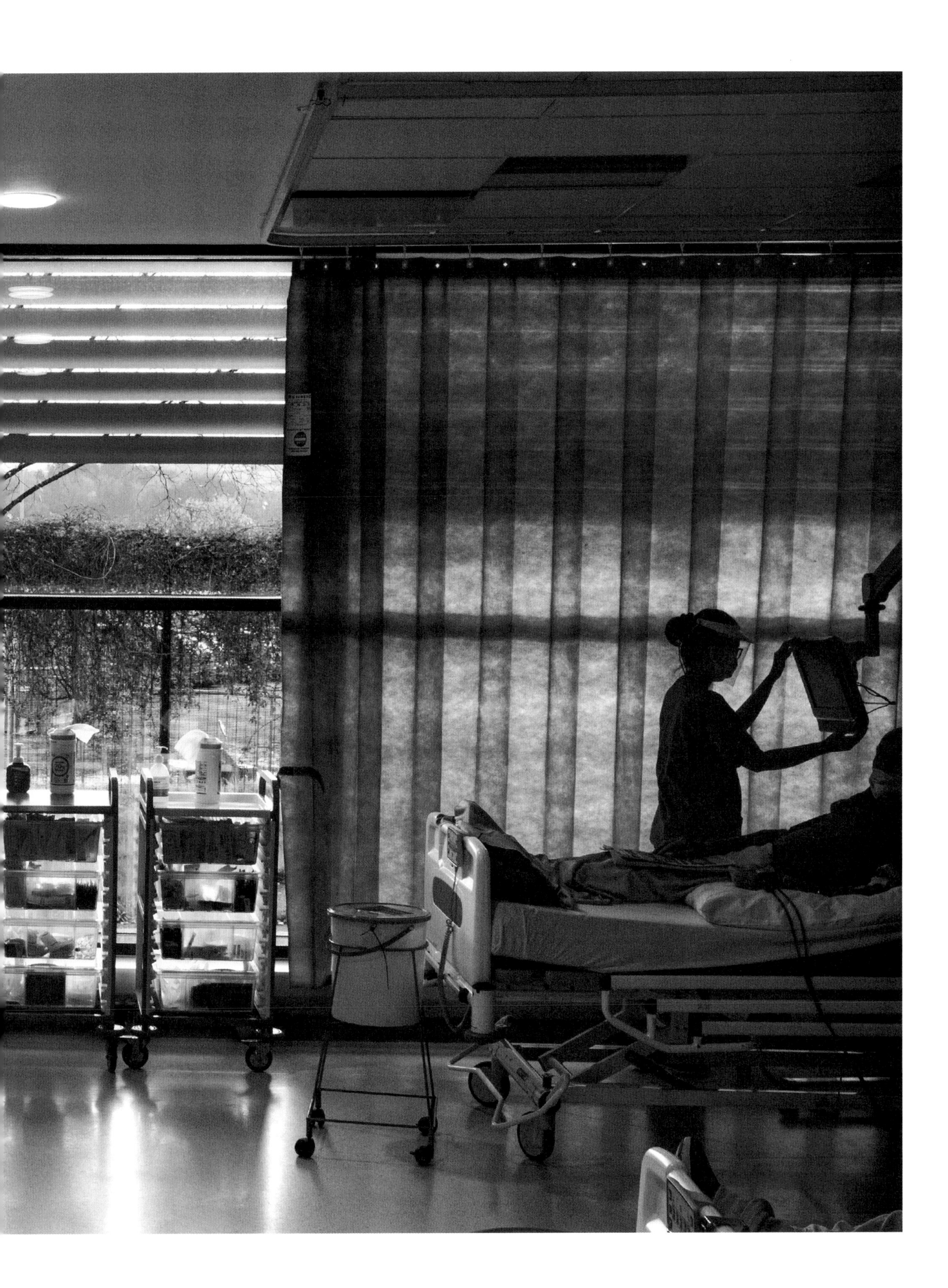

NHS

COVID-19 (coronavirus)
Everyone in Northern Ireland should now be using social distancing
Stay at least 2 metres (6 feet) away from other people
The Shop
Will be closing
today at 3.15
We apologise for any
inconvenience
Shop opening hours.
Monday to Sunday.
8am to 6.15pm
Coffee
STAFF only
HOT Water

Hairdressing Service
Vouchers for patients
available from
Front Hospital Shop
or
Snack Bars
HSC South Eastern Health and Social Care Trust
Only 2
customers
in the café
at any time
We apologise for
any inconvenience

door

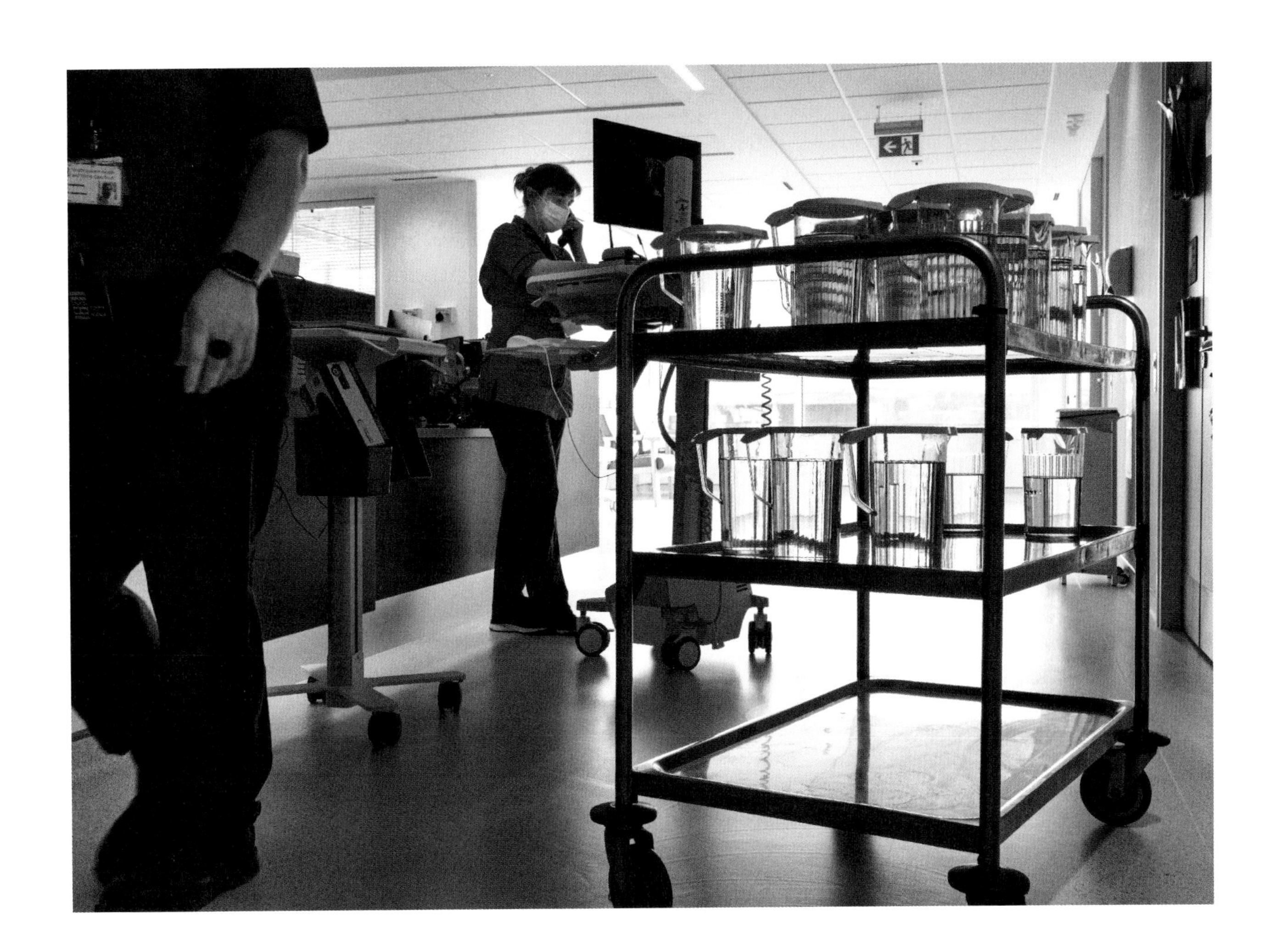

P
H

## OVERVIEW

In December 2019, reports emerged that a novel coronavirus had been identified in Wuhan, China. All this was happening thousands of miles away from Northern Ireland and life progressed as normal over Christmas 2019. However, there was greater unease as COVID-19 cases started appearing in Northern Italy during February and by March we were watching pictures of exhausted and traumatised intensive care doctors on social media and television screens.

On the week beginning 9 March it became inevitable that the virus was coming to the UK. Wards were emptied and elective procedures cancelled. Patients became too afraid to attend hospital and the Emergency Department was deserted. This was probably the most unsettling period of the pandemic. Staff were anxious and fearful of what was about to descend upon us. An eerie calm descended on empty corridors as we prepared for the unprecedented and unpredictable challenges that were to unfold. There was an absence of panic as we aimed to make a planned, structured and organised response to the anticipated surge in respiratory illness. The Infection Control department took centre stage and we were fit tested for masks and learned a new vocabulary of "donning" and "doffing" personal protective equipment (PPE). Signs appeared advising the maximum number of people allowed in each room and the social activities during breaks were greatly curtailed.

Daily virtual meetings from senior management removed uncertainty, helping to explain why actions were necessary and gave accurate information around patient numbers and availability of supplies. This clear and timely communication reduced barriers to change and enhanced the awareness of what others were doing. It helped connect the three hospital sites within the Trust and the community services around a common purpose. Staff responded magnificently to the need to move across and between hospital sites. They were supported by the deployment of interim Foundation Year 1 doctors and sixty 3rd and 4th year medical students as Medical Student Technicians.

There was reduced availability of outpatient facilities due to the lockdown. This was addressed by triaging referrals to consultants giving advice to GPs or arranging virtual or face to face consultations. Enhanced care in the community allowed earlier discharge and pre-operative assessment and day of surgery admission reduced bed pressures. The redeployment of theatre staff to ICU resulted in a reduction in the number of available operating lists. This was addressed by holding a weekly surgical scheduling meeting where theatre capacity was maximised and patients allocated slots on the basis of priority.

The Emergency Department developed a front door triage system to segregate patients into COVID and non-COVID areas. Acute Medicine moved from Wards 14/15 to Ward 4A to facilitate all admissions to single rooms to reduce the risk of cross infection. A cohesive pathway for patients enabled enhanced respiratory support on the wards and greatly reduced the number of patients requiring ICU. A senior respiratory team reviewed all COVID-19 patients requiring high oxygen therapy enabling them to be zoned appropriately and daily updates between respiratory and ICU consultants ensured timely transfer of patients into and out of ICU. Enhanced care pathways in the community enabled more timely discharge and helped reduce bed pressures.

In early December 2020 the best Christmas present arrived when vaccination started at the Ulster Hospital. This was a great morale booster and was followed by the SEHSCT being asked to manage the mass vaccination centre at the SSE arena. However, this was tempered by the tide of the second and then the third wave of the pandemic. This continued peak and trough and the prolonged nature of the pandemic has left staff tired and stressed.

The pandemic has had a massive impact on the Trust, its staff and patients resulting in a determination to build a better way of doing things going forward. Timely decision making which is clearly communicated to all those affected has become the norm. Although virtual platforms can never entirely replace face-to-face meetings, they have enabled staff to discuss matters in real time across the different specialties and sites and this can be built on further. The importance of good infection prevention and control has been recognised and has had the by-product of reducing the pre-pandemic nosocomial infections. Experience in the triage of GP referrals and use of virtual clinic reviews should reduce the need for patients to unnecessarily travel to outpatient clinics. Surgical scheduling and day surgery admissions can be developed further. Continued development of care in the community will help reduce bed pressures and enhance the well-being of those living within the Trust.

Staff working flexibly across and between sites will stand the Trust in good stead as it adapts to an increasingly changing environment. We have learned that staff are more successful carrying out familiar tasks in a new environment or a new task in their usual site than asking them to carry out a new role in an unfamiliar site. Nevertheless, bonds made between staff relocated at the height of the pandemic show the benefits of working as a single team for the good of our patients.

Perhaps the most enduring lesson so far is that staff, rather than oxygen, ventilators or beds, plays the most crucial part in the response to the pandemic.

Bob Darling
Associate Medical Director

# ACKNOWLEDGEMENTS

I am grateful to the SEHSCT for encouraging and allowing me to photograph on its premises throughout the pandemic. I particularly would like to thank Roisin Coulter, Charlie Martyn, Jane Loughrey, Jeanie Johnston, Donna McCabrey and Bob Darling.

I would like to thank all the members of the SEHSCT who contributed to the narratives and to all who appear in the photographs. It would have been meaningless without you.

I would also like to thank all the patients and their relatives who have consented to the photography and contributed to the narratives.

For their encouragement and guidance regarding photography and photobook publication, I am grateful to Leslie Armour, John Duffin, Clare Gallagher and the late Paul Hanley.

To my parents for putting a camera in my hands when I was 11 years old, thank you. You both continue to be a beacon of kindness and gentleness to those around you.

Last, but not least, the largest thanks to my wife, Merle, and children, Darrell, Katie and Callum. Nothing good happens without them.

Net proceeds from the sale of this book will be donated to Médecins Sans Frontières.

Order from www.tuckgoh.com

Designed by Sort Design

Printed by Gomer Press

This publication is printed on FSC certified paper

# IMAGE INDEX



AH Ards Hospital
DH Downe Hospital
LVH Lagan Valley Hospital
ED Emergency Department
UHD Ulster Hospital
ICU Intensive Care Unit
DPU Day Procedure Unit
PPE Personal Protective Equipment
CSSD Central Sterile Services Dept
QIIC Quality Improvement Innovation Centre
ICT Information Communication Technology
SEHSCT South Eastern Health and Social Care Trust

Ulster Hospital unless stated otherwise